D1207268

———— *Norton History of Science Library* ————

# WILLIAM HERSCHEL
## *and the Construction of the Heavens*

Norton History of Science Library

# WILLIAM HERSCHEL

## and the Construction of the Heavens

### MICHAEL A. HOSKIN

M.A., Ph.D., F.R.A.S.

*Lecturer in History of Science*
*Cambridge University*

*With Astrophysical Notes by*
### DR. D. W. DEWHIRST
*Cambridge Observatories*

W · W · NORTON & COMPANY · INC ·

NEW YORK

*for*
*Gerd Buchdahl*

COPYRIGHT © 1963 BY
*Oldbourne Book Co. Ltd.*

FIRST AMERICAN EDITION 1964

Library of Congress Catalog Card No. 64-10566

PRINTED IN THE UNITED STATES OF AMERICA

# Contents

# List of Plates

"It may indeed appear extraordinary that no mention should yet have been made of the great desiderata of astronomy,— those questions which have exercised the curiosity and employed the time and attention of astronomers ever since the science has assumed its present character—such as the parallax of the fixed stars, their proper motion, the motion or rest of our own system, and its connection with the rest of the universe. But these and many other points are too obviously suggested by their importance to need any particular notice or encouragement. The man, for whom discoveries of this class are reserved, soars far beyond any distinction which this society can bestow: the applause of the human race attends his labours; and no additional stimulus can be offered to those by which he is impelled."

From the Report to the First Annual General Meeting of the Astronomical Society of London, 9 February 1821, on subjects for the award of medals.[a]

[a] *Memoirs of the Astronomical Society of London*, 1 (1822–25), 24–5.

# Introduction

WILLIAM HERSCHEL was a giant among astronomers. He built huge telescopes, he used them to amass a vast natural history of the heavens, and he made this the springboard for daring interpretive papers that left his more cautious contemporaries uncertain what to think. Wrapped up though he personally was in his own researches, his work became the storm-centre of prolonged controversy. At the one extreme, the many hours of work he managed to pack into his day could only be admired; and it bore impressive fruit in long catalogues of various kinds and in many other discoveries of a factual nature, of which the planet Uranus and the existence of infra-red rays are only examples. At the other extreme he was given to flights of imagination: he might launch into speculations about lunar or solar inhabitants, and he was quite capable of discussing periodicity of Sun-spots on the basis of the prices of wheat at Windsor as reported by Adam Smith.

In between these extremes comes Herschel's exploration of "the construction of the heavens", that is, of the nature and distribution of celestial objects outside the confines of the solar system. Here he engaged in bold theory-construction, yet remained disciplined throughout by his unique experience as an observer. This book is a study, with documents, of his reports of this exploration, with emphasis on such matters as the questions he asked himself (and more particularly the questions he avoided asking), the assumptions he found necessary and the extent to which contrary facts were permitted to speak against them, and the way in which he marshalled (and occasionally suppressed) his evidence. I hope the results will interest the philosopher of science who is prepared to go out on fieldwork. In history of science an analysis such as this can help us to penetrate further into the development of Herschel's own thought, and it supplies additional, internal reasons for the surprisingly limited impact of this segment of Herschel's work on his contemporaries.

Although the relevant papers are notable documents in the history of astronomy, they have previously been available only in the volumes of the *Philosophical Transactions* where they first appeared, or in the rare collected edition by Dreyer published fifty years ago. The principal papers are therefore reprinted here. But more is needed, for even with Herschel's text before one it is difficult to get to grips with his thought unless one understands the nature of the examples he adduces. This is especially so with his work on nebulæ and star clusters, and even Dreyer in 1912 knew little more about the galactic or extra-galactic, gaseous or stellar, nature of some of the objects than Herschel did. Here I have been most fortunate in securing the co-operation of Dr D. W. Dewhirst of the Cambridge Observatories, who has supplied a large number of astrophysical notes (signed 'D') in which he identifies Herschel's objects and comments on his observations. To say of Herschel's massive 1811 paper that "most (but not all) of the nebulæ referred to in this paper we should now call galaxies" required a major piece of research, but it has opened our eyes to the fact that Herschel at this stage was looking at vast external galaxies comparable to our own and imagining that he was seeing single stars in the making! At the same time, to compare what we now know to have been visible through Herschel's telescopes with his own descriptions only increases our admiration for his visual acuity and practical insight. We sit in a warm library with the Palomar-N.G.S. Sky Survey; Herschel shivered all night at his telescope and thought of cures for ague.

The four surveys of Herschel's life and work that have appeared in recent years have made it possible for me in Chapter One to pass over his work on the solar system, on coloured rings in lenses, on infra-red rays, and so on, and to set the scene for what follows by outlining his early career, the strengths and defects of his character, and the persons and books with which he came into contact.

Chapters Two and Five centre on Herschel's career-long desire to establish a third dimension for the stars by determining their distribution in depth. At first he tried to apply the surveyor's method of triangulation to double stars on the supposition that one member of a typical double would be much nearer to us than the other. In the end his own observations showed that, in some cases at least, the members were rotating about each other at the same distance from us; and that he must therefore be satisfied with doing the best he could with the assumption that the stars in themselves are equally bright, so that their apparent brightness is a measure of their distance from us.

In the rigorous form that Herschel required and used, this assumption was actually disproved by his own work on double stars, but he resolutely closed his mind to this inconvenient fact. In any case, the assumption by itself was useless without some means of measuring the comparative brightness of stars, and this Herschel could only do in 1813, near the end of his life. Meanwhile, in place of a suitable photometric technique he had to make yet another assumption, that the traditional star magnitudes are measurements of brightness that provide a direct guide to distance; for years he flirted with a possible test for this dubious hypothesis, but he carried the test through only in 1817 —when the assumption was no longer necessary. Chapter Two also deals with Herschel's first and brilliant statistical attack on the problem of the direction of the solar motion, and with his later and ambiguous reworking of the problem.

Chapters Three and Four deal with Herschel's efforts to understand the thousands of nebulæ and star clusters he had discovered. He began by supposing that all nebulæ not clearly composed of stars were nevertheless very distant star systems, and he developed a theory of the evolution of star systems from

an initial, large-scale, near-uniform distribution towards individual, tightly-packed globular clusters. This suggested a spatial
as well as a temporal interpretation of his observations. Later,
when he realized that "true nebulosity" exists, he found himself no longer able to decide even in general terms the distance
of most nebulous objects: they might be near-by examples of
true nebulosity, or distant star systems as before. Accordingly
the spatial element of his theory becomes subordinate, and the
temporal one predominant: he handles each observed object as
though it were a photograph, and he orders the photographs
(as he thinks) chronologically, so as to show us first nebulæ
condensing into one or more stars and then the stars grouping
themselves into clusters.

Chapter Three also deals with Herschel's early mapping of
our Galaxy, founded on the assumptions that the stars are
roughly uniform in distribution throughout the Galaxy, and
that his telescopes could reach to the borders of the Galaxy in
all directions. Greatly underestimating the extent of our Galaxy,
he was able to compare it to other star systems—but no such
notable comparisons were possible after he later realized that
in fact our Galaxy was, for him, of indefinitely-great extent.

Dr Dewhirst has put me still further in his debt by his careful
reading of my typescript, which eliminated many errors, and
by his advice on numerous points; other valuable improvements
were kindly suggested by Mr R. M. Harré and Miss Christine
Jones. In the location of manuscripts I was greatly helped by
Dr Walter Cannon and Dr Michael G. Hall. I am indebted to
the Librarians of the Royal Society, the Royal Astronomical
Society, and the Linda Hall Library, for access to manuscript
material in their possession. Dr Cannon, Mr Peter F. Maggs,
and Mr Jacob Zeitlin helped me to trail Herschel's copy of
Wright's *An Original Theory* to its present owner, Mr S. I.
Barchas of Tucson, Arizona, who gave me every possible facility.

Cambridge, 1 June 1963                                    M.A.H.

# Chapter One

# *The Natural History of the Heavens*

---

IN 1781 the *Philosophical Transactions* contained a paper by a little-known amateur astronomer that began innocently enough, but was to prove one of the most remarkable in the history of astronomy.

## *Account of a Comet. By Mr. Herschel, F.R.S.; communicated by Dr. Watson, Jun. of Bath, F.R.S.*

(ON Tuesday the 13th of March, between ten and eleven in the evening, while I was examining the small stars in the neighbourhood of H Geminorum, I perceived one that appeared visibly larger than the rest: being struck with its uncommon magnitude, I compared it to H Geminorum and the small star in the quartile between Auriga and Gemini, and finding it so much larger than either of them, suspected it to be a comet.)

I was then engaged in a series of observations on the parallax of the fixed stars, which I hope soon to have the honour of laying before the Royal Society; and those observations requiring very high powers, I had ready at hand the several magnifiers of 227, 460, 932, 1536, 2010, &c. all which I have successfully used upon that occasion. The power I had on when I first saw the comet was 227. From experience I knew that the diameters of the fixed stars are not proportionally magnified with higher powers, as the planets are; therefore I now put on the powers of 460 and 932, and found the diameter of the comet increased in proportion to the power, as it ought to be, on a supposition of its not being a fixed star, while the diameters of the stars to which I compared it were not increased in the same ratio. Moreover, the comet being magnified much beyond what its light would admit of, appeared hazy and ill-defined with these great powers, while the stars preserved that lustre and distinctness which from many thousand observations I knew they would retain. The sequel has shewn that my surmises were well founded, this proving to be the Comet we have lately observed. . . .[1]

Scientific reporting in the eighteenth century did not culti-vate understatement such as we find today. Herschel gave his paper this unexciting title—"Account of a Comet"—because he thought it *was* unexciting: his French contemporary, Charles Messier, whom Louis XV nicknamed "the ferret of comets",[1a] was already well on the way towards discovering no less than twenty-one of these objects. Yet this apparently routine paper was to transform Herschel's whole life, for it was soon found that the supposed comet was a primary planet of the solar system, the one we know as Uranus and the very first to be discovered since recorded history began. No knowledge of astronomy was needed to appreciate the interest of the discovery: Herschel became famous almost overnight, and fame brought a tangible reward, in the shape of a royal pension sufficient for him to give up his career in music and devote his full time to what had hitherto been no more than his hobby of astronomy.

But to us the paper is significant much more for the foretaste it gives of what Herschel was to achieve in the future. The dis-covery, the paper showed, was the by-product of a series of observations not of members of the solar system (the main interest in astronomy at this period) but of the 'fixed' stars; further, these observations involved the use of a telescope of an optical perfection barely credible to contemporary opticians and astronomers; and, lastly, this instrument was in the hands of an observer of such great experience that he could recognize *at a glance* the difference between Uranus and a star.

In this book we are concerned with Herschel mainly as a

pioneer theorist, and we shall find that when he was theorizing he was fully prepared to speculate daringly about problems which have exercised astronomers ever since. As Sir Arthur Eddington remarked, "It cannot be denied that he was given to jumping to conclusions in a way which, when it comes off, we describe as profound insight, and when it does not come off, we call wild-cat speculation."[2] But we must never forget that underlying Herschel's conclusions was an immense wealth of factual information accumulated out of his own experience. In the "Account of a Comet" he was speaking no more than the sober truth about his observational work, although many of his contemporaries flatly refused to credit the magnifications he claimed: his friend William Watson summarized their view for him by saying, "Opticians think it no small matter, if they sell a Telescope w[hi]ch will magnify 60 or 100 times, & here comes one who pretends to have made some, which will magnify about 6000 times, is this credible?"[3] And Herschel was, to use his own metaphor, a natural historian of the heavens, a collector of observations. He was a man who would sit night after night at his instruments, often in great physical discomfort, year in and year out, whenever conditions allowed of observations. Typically, in 1786, when he moved house from Old Windsor to Slough, in the midst of all the upheaval "the last night at Clay Hall was spent in Sweeping [for nebulæ] till daylight, and the next the Telescope stud ready for observation at Slough".[4]

These sweeps were part of a systematic examination of the whole of the visible sky which began in 1783 and was not completed until 1802, when Herschel was in his sixty-fourth year. They were preceded by three 'reviews' of the sky, which Herschel described in a paper written early in 1783.

The first was made with a Newtonian telescope, something less than 7 feet focal length, a power of 222, and an aperture of $4\frac{1}{2}$ inches. It extended only to the stars of the first, second, third, and fourth magnitudes. Of my second review I have already given some account: it was made with an instrument much superior to the former, of 85·2 inches focus, 6·2 inches aperture, and power 227. It extended to all the stars in HARRIS's maps, and the telescopic ones near them, as far as the eighth magnitude. The catalogue of double stars, which I have had the honour of communicating to the Royal Society, and the discovery of the Georgium Sidus [Uranus], were the result of that review. My third review was with the same instrument and aperture, but with a very distinct power of 460, which I had already experienced to be much superior to 227, in detecting excessively small stars, and such as are very close to large ones. At the same time I had ready at hand smaller powers to be used occasionally after any particularity had been observed with the higher powers, in order to see the different effects of the several degrees of magnifying such objects. I had also 18 higher magnifiers, which gave me a gradual variety of powers from 460 to upwards of 6000, in order to pursue particular objects to the full extent of my telescope, whenever a favourable interval of remarkably fine weather presented me with a proper opportunity for making use of them. This review extended to all the stars in FLAMSTEAD's catalogue, together with every small star about them, as far as the tenth, eleventh, or twelfth magnitudes, and occasionally much farther, to the amount of a great many thousands of stars. To shew the practicability of what I have here advanced, it may be proper to mention, that the convenient apparatus of my telescope is such, that I have many a night, in the course of eleven or twelve hours of observation, carefully and singly examined not less than 400 celestial objects, besides taking measures of angles and positions of some of them with proper micrometers, and sometimes viewing a particular star for half an hour together, with all the various powers of my telescope.[5]

A letter written in 1785 by a visitor fills in the background to Herschel's account: "The thermometer in the garden stood at 13° Fahrenheit; but in spite of this, Herschel observes the whole night through, except that he stops every three or four hours and goes into the room for a few moments. For some years Herschel has observed the heavens every hour when the weather is clear, and this always in the open air, because he says that the telescope only performs well when it is at the same temperature as the air. He protects himself against the weather by putting on more clothing."[6] The same letter gives an insight into the unspectacular rewards of this perseverance: "I went to bed about one o'clock, and up to that time he had found that night four or five new nebulæ."

These systematic observations added over eight hundred new multiple stars to the few dozen previously known, and over two and a half thousand nebulæ and star clusters to the total of a hundred and three which Messier had listed because they were confusing his search for comets. In addition Herschel published in his lifetime four catalogues of the comparative brightness of stars and prepared two others,[7] and he took a large number of star counts which he used to explore the structure of the Galaxy (see Chapter Three). It was an extraordinary achievement, one that transformed the scale of existing knowledge of the stars and nebulæ. Hitherto they had been a happy hunting-ground for armchair philosophers, but for practising astronomers little more than a fixed and exceedingly remote backcloth to the motions of the planets which continental mathematicians were so triumphantly explaining in terms of Newtonian dynamics; now they were to become a regular field of astronomical inquiry.

In fact, the very first example of change among the stars to be recognized in the West since the second century before Christ was a nova which appeared in 1572, shortly followed by a second in 1604. What had seemed at first to be another nova, a star of the third magnitude in the constellation of the Whale which was observed in 1596 by David Fabricius and which faded and disappeared, reappeared in 1638 and proceeded to intrigue astronomers by its variations—Herschel's first published paper was to report his own observations of it.[8] As the decades passed a few other variable stars were discovered, and in Herschel's day they were being studied in England by Edward Pigott and by John Goodricke, a deaf mute who discovered the periodicity of the variations in Algol and explained them as caused by the interposition of a darker star between us and Algol.[9] In the colour of stars some supposed changes had been announced in 1760 by Thomas Barker on the basis of optimistic comparisons of modern observations with the uncertain descriptions given in classical poetry.[10] Changes in position had first been recognized only in 1718, when Halley compared the modern positions of Aldebaran, Sirius, and Arcturus with those agreed upon by ancient observers and found discrepancies which could only mean that they had shifted their position in the sky relative to the other stars.[11] Since then a few more 'proper' motions had been discovered, although it was uncertain to what extent these were only apparent and actually the result of the motion which the observers shared with the rest of the solar system.

These meagre fruits of prolonged and careful observations hardly offered a tempting prospect for an amateur astronomer with a busy musical practice; the progress made by earlier observers had been so slight that there was every likelihood of much work for small reward. That Herschel undertook the study of the fixed stars and then carried his programmes through to their conclusion reveals a fundamental element in his character, which we might call perseverance when it is admirable and obstinacy when it is not. Once his mind was made up, he allowed nothing—and no one—to stand in his way. At the time of the discovery of Uranus he was driven by a passion for building large telescopes to gather light from faint objects; neither a succession of spectacular disasters in the casting of disks for his mirrors nor the physical and mental strain of combining this work with a busy musical practice deflected him from his purpose,[12] and in the process he sacrificed his sister Caroline's career as a singer almost without noticing. Similarly, although new *evidence* might lead him to revise a theory he was not in the habit of listening to the opinions of others, and sometimes, as in his papers on the cause of coloured rings in lenses,[13] his stubborn rejection of every warning led him into unhappy controversy.

But without this rich endowment of perseverance Herschel might never have made a success of his musical career in England after he landed penniless in 1757 to escape from the troubles following the occupation of Hanover by the French. And, typically, during the years of struggle that followed he never lost the intellectual interests which had been aroused in childhood by his father, a Hanoverian gardener-turned-musician. This remarkable man was, reports his sister Caroline, "a great admirer of astronomy and had some knowledge of that science; for I remember his taking me on a clear frosty night into the street, to make me acquainted with several of the beautiful constellations, after we had been gazing at a comet which was then visible. And I well remember with what delight he used to assist my brother William in his philosophical studies, among which was a neatly turned globe, upon which the equator and the ecliptic were engraved by my brother."[14] William Herschel's teachers had fostered these intellectual interests to the point that when he was not yet eighteen years old he had taken advantage of a visit to England to learn the language and so read Locke's *Essay Concerning Human Understanding*! In a letter Herschel relates how in the early 1760s, when his musical duties took him on frequent journeys on horseback across the Yorkshire moors, he still found time first to master English and the Italian he needed in his work, and then to tackle Latin and even Greek. He continues: "The theory of music being connected with mathematics, had induced me very early to read in Germany all what had been written upon the subject of harmony; and when, not long after my arrival in England, the valuable book of Dr Smith's *Harmonics* came into my hands, I perceived my ignorance and had recourse to other authors for information, by which I was drawn from one branch of mathematics to another."[15] Turning to the years following 1766, when he was appointed organist at the fashionable Octagon Chapel at Bath, he goes on: "Among other mathematical subjects, Optics and Astronomy came in turn, and when I read of the many charming discoveries that had been made by means of the telescope, I was so delighted with the subject that I wished to see the heavens and Planets with my own eyes thro' one of those instruments."[16]

Among the brief autobiographical notes he preserved are isolated references to observations in 1766 of Venus and of an eclipse of the Moon.[17] The next mention of astronomy is to be found in Caroline's account of her second day in England, her brother having brought her over from Hanover in August 1772. The morning was devoted to lessons from Herschel in English, book-keeping, and singing, "and by way of relaxation we talked of Astronomy and the fine constellations with whom I had made acquaintance during the fine nights we spent on den Postwagen travelling through Holland".[18] On 19 April of the following year Herschel records that he bought a Hadley's quadrant and Emerson's *Trigonometry*, and on 10 May Ferguson's *Astronomy* and a book of astronomical tables.[19] Caroline tells us that in the spring of this year, with the end of the music season, she had hoped for more of her brother's attention. "I was greatly disappointed; for, in consequence of the harassing and fatiguing life he had led during the winter months, he used to retire to bed with a bason of milk or glass of water, and Smith's *Harmonics* and *Optics*, Ferguson's *Astronomy*, etc., and so went to sleep buried under his favourite authors; and his first thoughts on rising were how to obtain instruments for viewing those objects himself of which he had been reading."[20]

*A Compleat System of Opticks* by Robert Smith, Professor of Astronomy and Experimental Philosophy at Cambridge, had been published in two substantial quarto volumes in 1738. It provided the reader with comprehensive accounts of the theory of optics and of methods for the construction of telescopes and microscopes beginning with the grinding and polishing of glasses and ending with techniques for using the completed instruments. Herschel could scarcely have hit upon a book better suited to his needs, for it gave him just the grounding he needed for his work on the construction of telescopes. Now refracting telescopes had to be very long in order to minimize the effects of chromatic aberration—unless they were fitted with the recently invented compound lenses, and at this time Herschel was probably unaware of the existence of such lenses, which in any case were too small and expensive for him.[20a] And so, after spending the summer of 1773 trying out these long non-achromatic refracting telescopes, "about the 8th September I hired a two feet Gregorian one [which by use of a reflecting mirror avoided chromatic aberration]. This was so much more convenient than my long glasses that I soon resolved to try whether I could not make myself such another, with the assistance of Dr. Smith's popular treatise on *Optics*."[21] He then heard of tools and half-finished mirrors which a neighbour had for sale, and with these he began his own construction of mirrors. Experience and Dr Smith were the only teachers he required. Even when he was engaged three years later on the construction of very large instruments, "with the assistance of my mathematical knowledge, the *Optics* of Dr. Smith and *Mechanics* of Emerson, I found no difficulties but what I could get the better of".

But Smith was nothing if not thorough, and in Book IV of his treatise he provided a "history of telescopical discoveries in the heavens". The chapters on Sun, Moon, and planets were straightforwardly competent; the concluding chapter on "Telescopical discoveries in the Fixt Stars" opened up more possibilities. Smith described the number of stars revealed by the telescope, "the more of them as the aperture is more enlarged to take in more light",[22] and proved the immensity of the distances at which they lay. Bradley's careful observations of $\gamma$ Draconis had revealed no apparent shift as the Earth carried his telescope around the Sun, and he had estimated that if this shift had been as little as one second of arc he would have detected it; the star must therefore be *at least* 400,000 times as far from us as the Sun—but just how far no one knew.[23] Smith also mentioned three examples of "new stars", and the "lucid spots" observed in Orion, Andromeda, and elsewhere.[24]

A more comprehensive account of such discoveries was given by James Ferguson in his *Astronomy explained upon Sir Isaac Newton's principles*. This was a work of more popular stamp. Ferguson began life as a shepherd-boy, but became a teacher of astronomy and physics and an ingenious constructor of orreries and other mechanical models of celestial movements. His *Astronomy*, first published in 1756 and still appearing in new editions in the early nineteenth century, deals not only with the solar system but with the tides, the equation of time, the calculation of new and full Moons and eclipses, and of course descriptions of his mechanical models. In the single chapter "Of the fixed Stars", added for the second edition of 1757, he lists lucid spots and cloudy stars, new and variable stars, and changes of position among the stars, and he makes several suggestions which—*post hoc*, if not *propter hoc*—Herschel was later to explore. Like Smith, Ferguson reports the immense though uncertain distances of the nearest stars,[25] the determination of which Herschel made his first major task in astronomy. Like Smith, Ferguson links the aperture of a telescope with its ability to detect a faint object,[26] and herein lay the reason for Herschel's giant instruments. Ferguson points out that changes among the (apparent) positions of the stars could arise either from movement among the stars themselves or from the movement of the solar system,[27] a dilemma to the solution of which Herschel made major contributions (below, pp. 40–59). Variable stars, Ferguson believes, are slowly rotating on their axes,[28] and Herschel was to take the same view (below, p. 160).

At a more speculative level, Ferguson held that all planetary systems associated with stars are "provided with accommodations for rational inhabitants"; even comets, thought by William Whiston to be "so many hells for tormenting the damned with perpetual vicissitudes of heat and cold", are probably peopled with beings capable of appreciating God's handiwork[29] (a similar passion for populating the universe is to be found in Herschel's writings (below, p. 159); believing Sun-spots to represent glimpses of a temperate interior, he argued over and over again for the existence of life even on the Sun).[30] Associated with this conception in Ferguson's thought was the stable and harmonious structure of the universe: "Thousands of thousands of Suns, multiplied without end, and ranged all around us, at immense distances from each other, attended by ten thousand times ten thousand Worlds, all in rapid motion, yet calm, regular, and harmonious, invariably keeping the paths prescribed them; and these Worlds peopled with myriads of intelligent beings, formed for endless progression in perfection and felicity."[31] This expression of the order to be found in the essentially unchanging universe is typical of this period when scientific thinking was mechanical in inspiration and took clockwork as the outstanding model. It echoes a famous passage in Newton's *Opticks* (below, p. 66), in which the regularities in the planetary motions are taken as proof of the handiwork of an intelligent Creator—although this did not prevent Newton from requiring God to intervene and counteract perturbations in the solar system which he believed to be cumulative and so threatening its stability. But Ferguson, while accepting Newton's account of the mathematics of the situation, was (unlike Newton) prepared on occasion to submit to the implication of a future very different from the present: "Here we have a strong philosophical argument against the eternity of the World. For, had it existed from eternity, and been left by the Deity to be governed by the combined actions of the above forces or powers, generally called Laws, it had been at an end long ago. And if it be left to them it must come to an end. But we may be certain that it will last as long as was intended by its Author, who ought no more to be found fault with for framing so perishable a work, than for making man mortal."[32] Herschel, as we shall see (below, pp. 68–162), was one of those who did most to complete the transition in astronomy and make development in time—evolution—a familiar working concept.

These two books came into Herschel's hands at a period when he was eager to learn and so unusually receptive to the ideas of others. They contain many of the germs of Herschel's later interests, and it is difficult not to ascribe to them an influence on Herschel far beyond their merits as textbooks of optics and astronomy.

The discovery of Uranus ended Herschel's isolation as an astronomer in dramatic fashion. Leading observers at home and abroad wrote to find out who he was and what chance had led him to scrutinize so insignificant an object in the sky—though Herschel was quick to point out that the discovery was no accident, for sooner or later the planet's turn to be examined must have come.[33] But even before this, word of the remarkable musician-astronomer had begun to spread, and he had already been visited by the Astronomer Royal, the Secretary of the Royal Society, and the Director of the Oxford Observatory.[34] In 1779 he had happened to meet Dr William Watson, a prominent local resident and a Fellow of the Royal Society, who introduced him to the Bath Literary and Philosophical Society (at whom Herschel promptly unleashed a torrent of indifferent philosophical and scientific papers) and who communicated his more important discoveries to the Royal Society.

In the difficult years of transition that followed the discovery of Uranus, Watson proved an invaluable source of encouragement and political wisdom.[35] Self-taught as he was and remote from the London scientific world, Herschel lacked the professional's instinct for reporting research in a manner likely to find acceptance. Left to himself, he would link observations of mountains on the Moon with speculations about lunar inhabitants.[36] He supposed in his innocence that magnifications of thousands and clearly defined images of stars were too commonplace to require special justification. At the other extreme, in what was a theoretical paper "On the Parallax of the Fixed Stars" he gave a long description of his micrometer, the inclusion of which Watson warned him smacked of "charlatanerie"[37]. His writings often required modification before they were published, for at this period Herschel had little idea of what other astronomers had done or were doing; and he had been convicted of at least one serious error, when he had mistakenly reported a daily apparent movement of Uranus and so placed it much too near the Earth.[38]

It is not surprising, then, that the fantastic claims made by this unknown musician for his telescopes and the striking originality of many of his ideas led to violent controversy in Royal Society circles. Was he a genius, or "fit for Bedlam"[39] as many supposed? For the rest of his life Herschel was to be the subject of envious attacks—"Those who envy you for such there are," wrote Watson in 1789, "will sicken at the news [of the success of Herschel's new telescope], & will redouble their efforts in depreciating your merits"[40]—but at first even the most impartial astronomers were at a loss to know what to make of him.[41] Fortunately Watson was usually in the thick of the argument, begging Herschel's critics at least to suspend judgement, and meanwhile sending to Bath a stream of letters of encouragement and advice. He reported to Herschel criticisms of his papers,[42] and kept a lookout for the relevant publications of other astronomers.[43] He urged Herschel to earn the support of leading British and continental astronomers[44] by sending them the positions of double stars and asking them to verify these observations with their own instruments. He recommended him to clinch the matter by taking one of his telescopes to Greenwich for comparison with the Royal Observatory instruments, and went with Herschel on one of the visits,[45] which were an unqualified success.[46] He guided Herschel during the delicate negotiations which led to a royal pension and to Herschel's settling near Windsor in the summer of 1782 as a full-time astronomer.[47] Watson was a loyal ally, and it is sad to find their correspondence in later life degenerating into fruitless appeals from Watson for news of his too-preoccupied friend.[a]

Freed from his musical duties, Herschel quickly settled down to a vigorous routine that was to last for most of the forty years remaining to him: observations by night, often with the help of his faithful Caroline, and the day divided between the construction of telescopes whose sale would supplement his pension, and the writing up of his observations. Domestic events—the removals from Datchet to Old Windsor in 1785 and thence to Slough in 1786, Herschel's marriage to Mary Pitt in 1788, the birth of their son in 1792—scarcely interrupted the even tenor of his life, though as the years passed growing infirmities led to more frequent holidays, and Mary's private means happily relieved the need to build telescopes for sale.

The outstanding event of Herschel's later years was the construction of his mammoth telescope of 40-foot focal length, with mirrors of 48-inch diameter each weighing as much as a ton. It was much the largest instrument of the period, larger than any in Britain today. The King made two grants of £2000 each towards the cost and an annual allowance for its upkeep. Herschel himself planned and supervised the construction in every detail during the four years of building, and the completed instrument became one of the wonders of the age. Yet it was never a success. The single satisfactory mirror distorted under its own weight and tarnished easily, the machinery was awkward to handle, the time required for any form of regular sweeping impossibly great.[48] In addition, its completion coincided with Herschel's abandonment of the hypothesis that all nebulæ were formed of stars (below, pp. 117–29), an hypothesis the new telescope was ideally fitted to test. And so this monster, being of little practical use, became instead a monument to Herschel's limitless ambition to reach out into space.

[a] One later remark of Watson deserves mention. On 20 April 1802, he wrote: "Where Newton writes 'Hypotheses non *fingo*' it does not in my opinion imply that no hypothesis ought to be made, but that none ought to be *forged* or *feigned*."

# Chapter Two

# Double Stars and the Motion of the Sun

FROM ancient times through to the seventeenth century, those who had dared to speculate about the possible orbiting of the Earth about the Sun had been attacked on a variety of grounds, physical, astronomical, and religious. Of these counter-arguments, by far the most telling were physical: If the Earth is moving, it was said, how is it that a stone thrown straight up in the air keeps pace with the Earth and falls to the ground at the very place from which it was thrown?

But even within the restricted sphere of astronomy there was a simple and, it might be thought, decisive test which any observer could make. If the Earth is in orbit around the Sun, then when we look at the stars in January and again in July we are observing them from two points separated by a vast distance, twice that of the Earth from the Sun. This being the case, we ought to see an apparent difference in the positions of the stars, not because they have actually changed places but because our observation post has moved with the motion of the Earth (fig. 1).

Now if we make the appropriate observations of the stars and do *not* notice any apparent change among them, this *may* be because we are not moving after all, but it may equally be because we have simply failed to detect a change which is in fact

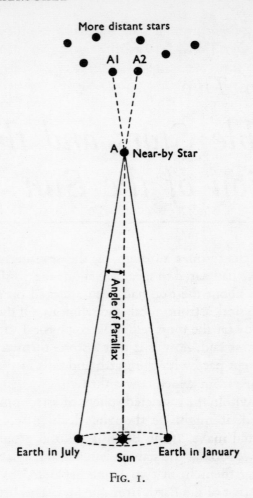

FIG. 1.

there. The farther the stars, the smaller any change and so the more accurate the observations required to detect it. In other words, though this test might seem at first sight to make possible a decisive refutation of the hypothesis of the motion of the Earth, an obstinate and unrepentant believer could always retort that the astronomers must go away and devise observations that were still more accurate.

Any plausibility this reply had once possessed had dwindled

to vanishing-point by the late sixteenth century when the Danish observer Tycho Brahe brought the accuracy of his instruments to somewhere near the limit of naked-eye observation; it now appeared as the unreasonable excuse of those who refuse to admit defeat. And then, quite suddenly, between the time of Galileo early in the seventeenth century and Newton towards the end, the whole controversy took a new turn. Developments in physics overtook and transformed the old arguments based on the behaviour of projectiles, and the evidence revealed by Galileo's telescope did much to discredit the Aristotelian cosmology which had required the Earth to be stationary in the middle of the world. It may be true that as late as 1760 Nevil Maskelyne, the Astronomer Royal, was still urging the need to vindicate Copernicus by the detection of the apparent annual change among the stars,[1] but for the great majority of physicists and astronomers the whole issue had long since been turned inside out. The search for the 'annual parallactic displacement' went on, but now for quite different reasons. The terrestrial observer, it was agreed, examined the stars from a platform moving in an orbit of known size. The importance of detecting the annual parallactic displacement of the nearer stars now lay in the urgent need for yardsticks to use in sidereal astronomy: for given this displacement and a little trigonometry, one could calculate the distance of the star from the Earth by the surveyor's method of triangulation. And until this was done the distances of the stars and their distribution in space must remain at best matters of intelligent inference from uncertain principles.

The problem, in this new form, had already defeated several generations of observers before Herschel appeared on the scene. It was clear that the angles to be measured were extremely small—as we have seen, James Bradley, third Astronomer Royal, concluded (after intensive efforts to detect the parallax of $\gamma$ Draconis with specially mounted telescopes and instruments had failed) that the displacement must be less than a single second (the greatest displacement of any star is the $1\frac{1}{2}$ seconds or, more exactly, twice $0''\cdot760$ of Proxima Centauri) and so the star must be more than 400,000 times as far as the Sun (the distance of Proxima Centauri is about two-thirds this figure);[a] and there were many sources of uncertainty quite apart from inaccuracies in the instruments themselves—for example in the refraction of the star's light as it passed through the Earth's atmosphere, and in the incompletely understood motions of the Earth's axis. In these circumstances it was not surprising that various astronomers, from Hooke and Flamsteed onwards, were deceived into thinking they had discovered examples of stellar parallax. At the time of Herschel's death the arguments were still raging, and in fact a valid case of parallax had yet to be detected.

Not that these efforts were without fruit. Bradley's patient work resulted in the discoveries both of the nutation of the Earth's axis and of the aberration of light, the latter an effect of the combination of the motion of the Earth with the motion of the light from the stars and so a physical confirmation of the Copernican hypothesis. And although Herschel failed in his immediate object he too, as we shall see, made important discoveries by way of compensation.

Herschel based his technique of investigation on the fact that many of the difficulties encountered in measuring stellar parallax were by-passed if the astronomer concentrated not on the absolute position of the star but on the *difference* between the positions of two stars lying close together in the sky. Each of the positions would be affected similarly by such effects as atmospheric refraction, and so the influence of these complications on the (small) difference between these positions would be negligible. The convenience of this type of measurement in the detection of stellar parallax had been suggested by Galileo[2] (who

[a] At first Herschel hoped that some stars would have a (total) displacement of more than one second (*Phil. Trans.*, LXXII (1782), 85–6; Dreyer, I, 41); later he too accepted one second as the maximum (below, p. 170).

of course did not know just how many interfering factors are avoided by this method) and by many astronomers since. *Provided* the two stars merely happened by chance to lie in the same direction from Earth and were not actually close together in space, then the parallax of the nearer would be greater than that of the more distant and the difference should be relatively easy to detect. In fact for practical purposes the more distant star would have no measurable parallax and so would act as a fixed point by which to measure the parallax of the nearer.

Now it seemed obvious that, generally, the brightest stars are those nearest to us, and therefore the ones with the greatest parallax. For comparison distant—and presumably faint—stars were needed lying in the same direction as the bright ones. Accordingly, in 1747 Bradley urged astronomers to "examine nicely the relative Situations of particular Stars: and especially of those of the greatest Lustre, which, it may be presumed lie nearest to us, and may therefore be subject to more sensible Changes", and at the same time to "determine the relative Positions of some of the *smallest* [faintest] that appear near them".[3]

Twenty years later, when Herschel appeared on the scene, no progress had been made. With characteristic courage and self-confidence he promptly took the determination of stellar distances as his first major task in astronomy and decided to tackle it by this method of *double stars*. Accordingly, during his second review of the heavens which took from 1779 to 1781, he kept careful watch for multiple stars, especially double stars in which the two members were very different in brightness (and so presumably in distance) and were also close to each other in the sky. His search thus far resulted in his first catalogue of two hundred and sixty-nine double stars, read before the Royal Society on 10 January 1782. On 6 December 1781, but after the manuscript had been delivered, his faithful friend William Watson had heard that Christian Mayer of Mannheim had also published a catalogue of double stars, and to discover more of this Watson duly presented himself for breakfast next morning at the home of Sir Joseph Banks, the President of the Royal Society.[4] Banks gave Watson a copy of Mayer's catalogue to lend to Herschel, who had Caroline copy it;[5] but fortunately there was little overlap, and moreover Herschel's doubles were closer together than Mayer's and so more suitable for the sensitive measurements Herschel had in mind.

Herschel explained the motives behind his current investigations in a paper "On the Parallax of the Fixed Stars"[6] read before the Royal Society on 6 December 1781. It was intended to set the scene for his first catalogue of double stars by discussing the advantages of this method for determining parallax, describing his micrometer and other apparatus, and developing the elementary mathematics which would be needed to convert parallactic displacements into measurements of distances.

On 19 April, Maskelyne wrote to Herschel a long and friendly letter[7] reporting the views of the Royal Society Publications Committee and the improvements they suggested. In particular, they were unhappy about the two postulates on which Herschel had based his mathematical treatment. These were: "1. Let the stars be supposed, one with another, to be about the size of the sun. 2. Let the difference of their apparent magnitudes [the traditional classification of the stars by decreasing brightness] be owing to their different distances, so that a star of the second, third, or fourth magnitude is two, three, or four times as far off as one of the first."[8] Maskelyne and his Committee felt that the first postulate was unnecessarily strong,[9] and that the second was positively false. Herschel was referred to a remarkable paper (which the faithful Caroline was required to copy)[10] by the Rev. John Michell, "An Inquiry into the probable Parallax, and Magnitude of the fixed Stars, from the Quantity of Light which they afford us, and the particular Circumstances of their Situation", published in the *Philosophical Transactions* in 1767.[11]

Michell agreed that generally brightness was an index of nearness. "In the meantime, till this parallax can be found, or something else may arise to furnish us with a more general analogy, we can only suppose them [the stars], at a medium, to be equal in size to the Sun, this being the best means, which we have at present of forming some probable conjecture concerning the extent of the visible universe."[12] Michell knew of the pioneer study in photometry by Pierre Bouguer,[13] and had himself devised a rough way of estimating the distances of the brightest stars. He had asked himself how far away the Sun would have to be removed before it appeared as a bright star, and had resolved the question by making Saturn the bridge for comparing the brightness of the Sun and the stars: Saturn in opposition was as bright as a first-magnitude star, and Saturn's brightness depended upon the brightness of the Sun. The figure he arrived at for the distance of Sirius was about 20 million million miles, but as he remarked, this had to be multiplied by a factor to allow for Saturn's absorption of light.[a] In fact Sirius is some 50 million million miles away, so that Michell, like Bradley, had a remarkably good idea of stellar distances decades before the discovery of an example of annual parallax.

So far so good; but there were two later points in the paper which threatened Herschel's position: Michell's estimates of comparative brightnesses of stars, and the significance he attached to groupings among the stars. Michell, like Herschel, understood very well that for the present, if one was to study the distribution of the stars in depth, one must first make the *assumption* that the stars vary little among themselves. One was then left with the *practical* problem of actually making these comparisons of brightness. Exact measurements of starlight were needed, "that, instead of distributing them [the stars], as has hitherto

---

[a] Similar methods were used with success by J. P. L. de Cheseaux (1744), Lambert (1760), and Olbers (1801). See F. G. W. Struve, *Études d'astronomie stellaire* (St Petersburg, 1847), note 95.

been done, into a few ill-defined classes, they may be ranked with precision both according to their respective brightness, and the exact degree of it".[14]

Michell had made some rough measurements, and, as Maskelyne pointed out, his results contradicted Herschel's second postulate. Michell believed, "according to the best judgment I have been able to make from some gross experiments", that first-magnitude stars were from 400 to 1000 times brighter than sixth-magnitude stars, the faintest visible to the naked eye. On the assumption that one star is much the same as another in size and intrinsic luminosity, so that the differences we observe in their brightnesses are due simply to differences in their distances from us, these comparisons of brightness could be translated into comparisons of distance; and since brightness falls off with the square of the distance, Michell concluded that sixth-magnitude stars were from $\sqrt{400}$ to $\sqrt{1000}$ times farther than first-magnitude stars—say an average of twenty-five times, in contrast to Herschel's figure of six.[15]

Today first- and sixth-magnitudes are *defined* so that, other things being equal, a sixth-magnitude star is ten times farther than one of the first magnitude. In the eighteenth century the classifications were vague, as both men knew, but at least Herschel's figure of six was no worse than Michell's twenty-five. No doubt Herschel's already wide experience as an observer reinforced his customary scepticism towards the results of others, but he short-circuited the discussion by adding a footnote to his paper which in effect *defined* magnitudes to give the distances he required: he "rather meant the order into which the stars *ought to be* distinguished than that into which they *are* commonly divided: for as the order of the magnitudes is here to denote the different relative distances, we are to examine carefully the degree of light each star is accurately found to have: and considering then that light diminishes in the inverse ratio of the squares of the distances, we ought to class the stars accordingly".[16] In this way he prevented any argument. But he was of course still left with the practical problem of the exact measurement of starlight, and during the many years of unsuccessful experiments in photometry that lay ahead he continued to use the traditional apparent magnitudes as though they were equivalent to his defined ones. Even when on one occasion he does explicitly employ his defined magnitudes, he smuggles in his postulate by employing star counts based on the traditional magnitudes![17]

What could Herschel have done to decide between himself and Michell? Oddly enough, the answer lay in a paper which Herschel quoted to Maskelyne in support of his *first* postulate: "The Number, Order, and Light, of the Fix'd Stars", by Edmond Halley.[18] Halley had asked himself whether it is possible that the stars are distributed at more or less regular intervals throughout space, and he had tested this model by examining the geometry of points regularly distributed. Taking one point as the Sun and the nearest points as corresponding to the nearest stars, he had predicted from the model the number of stars nearest to the Sun. He had then assumed that such stars were the brightest (first magnitude), and in this way had been able successfully to relate his prediction from the model to the number of observed first-magnitude stars, and so confirm the model. Halley continued:

If therefore the Number of them be supposed Thirteen, . . . at twice the distance from the Sun there may be placed four times as many, or 52; which, with the same allowance, would nearly represent the number of the Stars we find to be of the 2d magnitude: so 9 × 13, or 117, for those at three times the distance: and at ten times the distance 100 × 13 or 1300 Stars; which distance may perhaps diminish the light of any of the Stars of the first magnitude to that of the sixth,[a] it being but the hundredth part of what, at the present distance, they appear with.

[a] It is difficult not to be impressed with the way in which Halley's estimate corresponds exactly to the modern definition of magnitudes.

Herschel, by working along these lines and assuming the validity of the model out to a distance of only six times that of first-magnitude stars, could have tested his second postulate; and, as we shall see, at this period he thought the model was valid for the full extent of the Galaxy. Yet although he flirted with the test from time to time, he grasped the nettle firmly only at the very end of his life, when it could no longer harm him, for he already knew the right answer on other grounds (below, pp. 171–4).

The Halley model represented uniformity of spatial distribution; essential though it was for Herschel's "delineation of our nebula" or Galaxy (below, pp. 87–96), it was for most purposes an expendable hypothesis against which to match observations designed to establish the construction of the heavens. But Herschel assumed uniformities whenever there was no compelling evidence to the contrary, and it was only after prolonged years of searches for nebulæ and star clusters— that is, for non-uniformities of distribution—that he recognized how limited were the valid applications of the Halley model. Michell, on the other hand, was very conscious of groupings among the stars, and in a passage that threatened to undermine much of Herschel's work he argued that the odds against these groupings being only apparent and due simply to the chance position of the terrestrial observer were overwhelming:

If we now compute, according to the principles above laid down, what the probability is, that no two stars, in the whole heavens, should have been within so small a distance from each other, as the two stars β Capricorni, to which I shall suppose about 230 stars only to be equal in brightness, we shall find it to be about 80 to 1. For an example, where more than two stars are concerned, we may take the six brightest of the Pleiades, and, supposing the whole number of those stars, which are equal in splendor to the faintest of these, to be about 1500, we shall find the odds to be near 500000 to 1, that no six stars, out of that number, scattered at random, in the whole heavens, would be within so small a distance from each other, as the Pleiades are. . . . We may from hence, therefore, with the highest probability conclude (the odds against the contrary opinion being many millions to one) that the stars are really collected together in clusters in some places, where they form a kind of system, whilst in others there are either few or none of them, to whatever cause this may be owing, whether to their mutual gravitation, or to some other law or appointment of the Creator. And the natural conclusion from hence is, that is is highly probable in particular, and next to a certainty in general, that such double stars, &c. as appear to consist of two or more stars placed very near together, do really consist of stars placed near together, and under the influence of some general law, whenever the probability is very great, that there would not have been any such stars so near together, if all those, that are not less bright than themselves had been scattered at random through the whole heavens.[19]

If Michell was right—and Herschel was well able to follow his argument—then it meant that, in the first place, nearly all of Herschel's double stars were in fact physical systems revolving about their common centre of gravity, and so useless for the purposes Herschel had in mind. There were to be no misunderstandings about it, for Michell in 1783 wrote praising Herschel's work, but reminding readers of his own earlier paper, saying "it is not improbable, that a few years may inform us, that some of the great number of double, triple, stars, etc., which have been observed by Mr. Herschel, are systems of bodies revolving about each other".[20]

When Herschel's first catalogue of double stars was read before the Royal Society in January 1782, he probably did not yet know of Michell's paper. In a postscript to the catalogue he explained that he had been careful to use the neutral term *double star*, which did not suggest any necessary physical relationship such as Christian Mayer had argued, it being "much too soon to form any theories of small stars revolving round large ones".[21] But he admitted privately to von Zach that he suspected Rigel to have a satellite, an opinion which was revealed to the public in 1786 in *Astronomisches Jahrbuch* for 1789.[21a] Yet he continued to search for double stars, and sought to apply them to the detection of the motion of the solar system, long after reading Michell's powerful arguments. Twenty years later, when his long years of sweeping for nebulæ had come to an end, he returned to his double stars and found (as Michell had forecast) that a few of them had already altered position relative to each other in a way that could only be explained by their rotation round each other.[22] In this way he contributed a link to the chain extending Newtonian gravitation beyond the solar system. The fact that the stars occur in clusters had already strongly suggested the presence of attractive forces at great distances from Earth, and, on the other hand, the proof that double stars were actually moving under the inverse-square law of Newtonian gravitation was to await the accurate positional astronomy of the decades following Herschel's death; but now at last stars had actually been *seen* moving round each other, and the binary systems made probable by Michell were an observed reality.

In making the first public announcement of these observations,[23] Herschel produced probability arguments of his own in favour of binary systems! Why, then, did he not give more weight to Michell's paper when he first read it twenty years before?

There is no simple answer to this question. Michell's argument applied to double stars *in general*, whereas Herschel's original purposes involved individual pairs only: it mattered little if many doubles were binary systems, provided some were merely chance or 'optical' doubles. And in his later work Herschel distinguishes many times, as Michell does not, between doubles in regions where there are few stars and so optical doubles are unlikely, and those in regions near the densely-populated Milky Way where he continues to expect a number of optical doubles.[24] In any case, Herschel's temperament made him disinclined to learn from others, especially when he was well launched on a problem; as with the controversy over his second postulate, he preferred to face threats to his programme of work only when there was no longer anything to be lost. But the question may also have been linked in Herschel's mind with a far more fundamental threat posed by Michell's work, one which he chooses to ignore even when he has himself observed binary stars: namely, that star systems are often composed of stars of very different brightnesses *even though* they are at about the same distance from us. In other words, if the stars of the Pleiades, or of a binary system with unequal members, are at about the same distance from us and *yet* appear to be of different brightnesses, then this demonstrates that brightness is not a reliable guide to distance.

Michell had been perfectly willing to concede "a very great difference" among the stars;[25] Herschel, caught up in a full-scale investigation of the distribution of the stars in depth, could allow himself no such liberty. Without the principle that 'brightness equals nearness', as we might term it, he could not even *embark* on the task of providing a third dimension to sidereal astronomy. In any case the surveyor's method of triangulation, although giving absolute and not merely relative distances, is only feasible with comparatively near objects. In fact the principle that 'brightness equals nearness' is used today to measure large astronomical distances, the difference being that whereas Herschel thought of *all* stars as forming a single species and therefore similar in brightness (see, for example, below, p. 174), we now measure large distances by means of RR Lyrae stars, blue giants, and other members of what we might describe as true species. Herschel, after all, was not to know that stars vary enormously in brightness, so that one may be a million times brighter than the Sun while another is several thousand times less bright.

On the other hand, Herschel in 1806 knew perfectly well when he used the estimated brightnesses of stars to establish their relative distances to *three significant figures*[26] that the binary systems he had established three years before included γ Leonis (catalogued as "pretty unequal"[27] and referred to as "this star and its small companion"),[28] ε Bootis ("very unequal"),[29] and α Herculis ("very unequal",[30] of which "the two stars are sufficiently different in magnitude, for us to expect a difference in parallax, on a supposition that their distances from us are inversely as their apparent magnitudes").[31] Herschel's earlier belief that he had proved the stars of a globular cluster to be of almost identical size (below, p. 109) can scarcely have been held sufficient to outweigh this very specific evidence: his friend Professor Vince of Cambridge accepted the inference from the evidence of the globular cluster, but still maintained "we have no reason whatever" for supposing that 'brightness equals nearness'.[32]

The principle took another hard knock in 1812, when F. W. Bessel announced that the faint star 61 Cygni had the enormous annual proper motion of over 5″,[33] and drew the correct and natural conclusion that the star must be near to us *in spite of its faintness*; yet in his 1817 and 1818 papers Herschel was still applying the principle rigorously, for example remarking even of stars of the same (first) magnitude that "their very different lustre will not allow us to suppose them to be at equal distances from us" (below, p. 171). Herschel's ability to close his mind to inconvenient facts is truly impressive.

But this was for the future. Meanwhile, Herschel was considering other applications of his double stars. They could, he suggested in his parallax paper, be used to detect not merely the orbital motion of the observer round the Sun but *any* motion of the observer in which the double stars did not share—in particular, the motion of the solar system relative to the neighbouring stars.[34] Herschel (not without reason) regarded his conception as daring, and although Maskelyne had told him of Michell's interest in the subject[35] it was only after his paper on solar motion had been sent to the Royal Society that he learned that several other astronomers[36] had been thinking about the same question.

In this paper, Herschel not only paved the way for a future determination of the motion of the solar system on the basis of possible changes in the double stars, but launched an *immediate* attack on the problem in terms of the known proper motions of the stars. Here, we must emphasize, he and other astronomers were competing on level terms: for once Herschel could not exploit his unique command of observational astronomy. The necessary facts were public knowledge, the mathematics required were elementary. It was Herschel who had the insight and the courage to draw out the implications.

The root of the problem, how to disentangle the true proper motions of the stars from the apparent motions which reflect the motion of the solar system, had been clearly put by Bradley in 1748:

> If our own Solar System be conceived to change its Place, with respect to Absolute Space; this might, in Process of Time, occasion an apparent Change in the angular Distances of the fixed Stars; and in such a Case, the Places of the nearest Stars being more affected, than of those that are very remote; their relative Positions might seem to alter; tho' the Stars themselves were really immoveable. And on the other Hand, if our own System be at Rest, and any of the Stars really in Motion, this might likewise vary their apparent Positions; and the more so, the nearer they are to us, or the swifter their Motions are, or the more proper the Direction of the Motion is, to be rendered perceptible by us.[37]

Various speculations about the Sun's motion appeared in the next few years, and in 1760 Tobias Mayer of Göttingen described the form which the stellar motions reflecting the motion of the solar system would take. He did this by analogy with a man walking through a forest, the trees in front of him appearing to open out at his approach while those he is leaving behind appear to close up. But Mayer failed to make full allowance for the very imperfect state of contemporary knowledge of the proper motions of fixed stars, and since there was then little evidence of a concerted movement among the stars, he concluded the solar system was in fact at rest.[38] Michell, in his 1767 paper, also discussed the problem of disentangling the reflected solar motion from the true motions of the stars, and he suggested that a knowledge of the direction and velocity of the solar motion would in time help in determining the distance of the more remote stars.[39]

Herschel, as we have seen, was already thinking about this problem before he learned of Michell's work. Somewhat aghast at his own daring, at the beginning of his paper he gently introduced the reader to the idea of solar motion by listing some of the other changes observed among the stars, arguing that it would be unreasonable to exempt the Sun from this general rule of change. Without giving the matter much thought Herschel at once assumed that all these changes were to be explained on the 'brightness equals nearness' principle (below, p. 54), although Maskelyne was quick to point out the absurd motions this would require and Herschel agreed to amend this passage. Maskelyne also suggested[40] that the list should be published separately, but although Herschel preferred[41] instead to enlarge his title the list is not germane to the paper and is here omitted. Herschel then outlined the theory on which he was working by showing how the Sun's motion will be reflected in a general tendency among the fixed stars to open out in front of the Sun and close in behind, and followed this with a list, for the convenience of later observers, of double stars particularly well situated for detecting solar motion. He then concluded by applying his general theory to the small number of proper motions known to him and showing in brilliant style that *if* the Sun was moving to a point near $\lambda$ Herculis *then* the proper motions of near-by stars would have the general pattern that had in fact been observed.

*On the proper Motion of the Sun and Solar System; with an Account of several Changes that have happened among the fixed Stars since the Time of Mr. Flamstead.*[a]

## By William Herschel, Esq. F.R.S.

Read March 6, 1783.

THE new lights that modern observations have thrown upon several interesting parts of astronomy begin to lead us now to a subject that cannot but claim the serious attention of every one who wishes to cultivate this noble science. That several of the fixed stars have a proper motion is now already so well confirmed, that it will admit of no further doubt. From the time this was first suspected by DR. HALLEY we have had continued observations that shew Arcturus, Sirius, Aldebaran, Procyon, Castor, Rigel, Altair, and many more, to be actually in motion; and considering the shortness of the time we have had observations accurate enough for the purpose, we may rather wonder that we have already been able to find the motions of so many, than that we have not discovered the like alterations in all the rest. Besides, we are well prepared to find numbers of them apparently at rest, as, on account of their immense distance, a change of place cannot be expected to become visible to us till after many ages of careful attention and close observation, though every one of them should have a motion of the same importance with Arcturus. This consideration alone would lead us strongly to suspect, that there is not, in strictness of speaking, one *fixed* star in the heavens; but many other reasons, which I shall presently adduce, will render this so obvious, that there can hardly remain a doubt of the general motion of all the starry systems, and consequently of the solar one among the rest.

I might begin with principles drawn from the theory of attraction, which evidently oppose every idea of absolute rest in any one of the stars, when once it is known that some of them are in motion: for the change that must arise by such motion, in the value of a power which acts inversely as the squares of the distances, must be felt in all the neighbouring stars; and if these be influenced by the motion of the former, they will again affect those that are next to them, and so on till all are in motion.

a [*Phil. Trans.*, LXXIII (1783), 247–83.]

WILLIAM HERSCHEL

Now as we know several stars, in divers parts of the heavens, do actually change their place, it will follow, that the motion of our solar system is not a mere hypothesis; and what will give additional weight to this consideration is, that we have the greatest reason to suppose most of those very stars, which have been observed to move, to be such as are nearest to us; and therefore, their influence on our situation would alone prove a powerful argument in favour of the proper motion of the sun, had it actually been originally at rest. But I shall waive every view of this subject which is not chiefly derived from experience. . . .

[Herschel outlines his reviews of the heavens (above, pp. 15–16), and then lists changes already observed among the stars.]

To return to the principal subject of this paper, which is the proper motion of the sun and solar system: does it not seem very natural, that so many changes among the stars,—many increasing their magnitude, while numbers seem gradually to vanish;—several of them strongly suspected to be new-comers, while we are sure that others are lost out of our sight;— the distance of many actually changing, while many more are suspected to have a considerable motion:—I say, does it not seem natural that these observations should cause a strong suspicion that most probably every star in the heaven is more or less in motion? And though we have no reason to think,[a] that the disappearance of some stars, or new appearance of others, nor indeed the frequent changes in the magnitudes of so many of them are owing to their change of distance from us by proper motions, which could not occasion these phenomena without being inconceivably quick; yet we may well suppose, that motion is some way or other concerned in producing these effects. A slow motion, for instance, in an orbit round some large opaque body, where the star, which is lost or diminished in magnitude, might undergo occasional occultations, would account for some of those changes, while others might perhaps be owing to the periodical return of large spots on that side of the surface which is alternately turned towards us by a rotatory motion of the star. The idea also of a body much flattened by a quick rotation, and having a motion similar to the moon's orbit by a change of the place of its nodes, whereby more of the luminous surface would one time be exposed to us than another, tends to the same end; for we cannot help thinking with M. DE LA LANDE (*Mem.* 1776), that the same force which gave such rotations, would probably also occasion motions of a different kind by a translation of the

a [Herschel changed his mind after drafting this paper. His original version, in which he seeks to explain these changes in a manner compatible with the 'brightness equals nearness' principle, is reproduced on p. 54.]

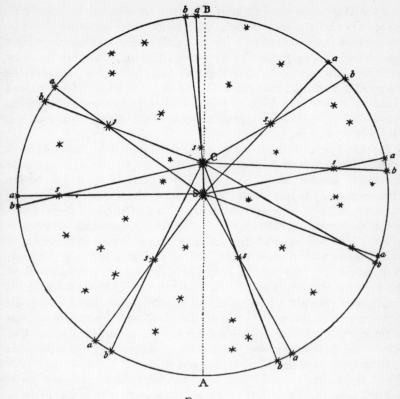

FIG. 2.

center.[a] Now, if the proper motion of the stars in general be once admitted, who can refuse to allow that our sun, with all its planets and comets, that is, the solar system, is no less liable to such a general agitation as we find to obtain among all the rest of the celestial bodies?[b]

Admitting this for granted, the greatest difficulty will be how to discern the proper motion of the sun between so many other (and variously

[a] Relating to the motion of the fixed stars, the Astronomer Royal has an expression in the second page of the explanation and use of the tables published in his *Astronomical Observations*, which seems to favour this idea, where he mentions the "peculiar but small motions, which many, IF NOT ALL OF THEM, have among themselves, which have been called their *proper motions*, the causes and laws of which are hid for the present in almost equal obscurity."

[b] See MR. MICHELL'S note, *Phil. Trans.* vol LVII. p. 252.

compounded) motions of the stars. This is an arduous task indeed, which we must not hope to see accomplished in a little time; but we are not to be discouraged from the attempt. Let us, at all events, endeavour to lay a good foundation for those who are to come after us. I shall therefore now point out the method of detecting the direction and quantity of the supposed proper motion of the sun by a few geometrical deductions, and at the same time shew by an application of them to some known facts, that we have already some reasons to guess which way the solar system is probably tending its course.

Suppose the sun to be at S, fig. 2; the fixed stars to be dispersed in all possible directions and distances around at $s, s, s, s$, &c. Now, setting aside the proper motion of the stars, let us first consider what will be the consequence of a proper motion in the sun; and let it move in a direction from A towards B. Suppose it now arrived at C. Here, by a mere inspection of the figure, it will be evident, that the stars $s, s, s$, which were before seen at $a, a, a$, will now, by the motion of the sun from S to C, appear to have gone in a contrary direction, and be seen at $b, b, b$; that is to say, every star will appear more or less to have receded from the point B, in the order of the letters $ab, ab, ab$. The converse of this proposition is equally true; for if the stars should all appear to have had a retrograde motion, with respect to the point B, it is plain, on a supposition of their being at rest, the sun must have a direct motion towards the point B, to occasion all these appearances. From a due consideration of what has been said, we may draw the following inferences.

1. The greatest or total systematical parallax of the fixed stars, fig. 3, will fall upon those that are in the line DE, at rectangles to the direction AB of the sun's motion.

2. The partial systematical parallax of every other star, $s, s, s$, not in the line DE, will be to the total parallax as the sine of the angle BS$a$, being the star's distance from that point towards which the sun moves, to radius.

3. The parallax of stars at different distances will be inversely as those distances; that is, one half at double the distance, one third at three times, and so on; for the subtense SC remaining the same, and the parallactic angle being very small, we may admit the angle S$s$C, to be inversely as the side S$s$, which is the star's distance.

4. Every star at rest, to a system in motion, will appear to move in a direction contrary to that in which the system is moving.

Corollary. Hence it follows, that if the solar system be carried towards any star situated in the ecliptic: every star, whose angular distance *in antecedentia* (reckoned upon the ecliptic from the star towards which the system moves) is less than 180 degrees, will decrease in longitude. And

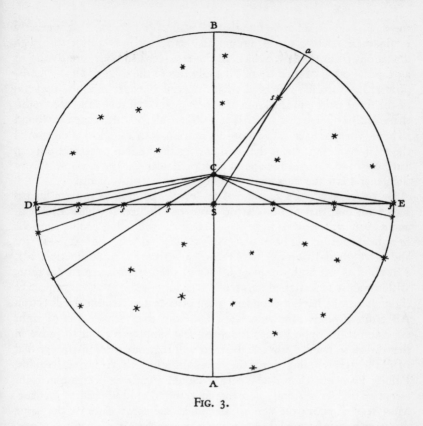

FIG. 3.

that, on the contrary, every star, whose distance from the same star (reckoned upon the ecliptic but *in consequentia*) is less than 180 degrees, will increase in longitude, in both cases without alteration of latitude. . . .

[Herschel lists double stars well placed to reveal the motion of the solar system after a few years of observations, and then returns to his main theme.]

It remains now only for me to make an application of this theory to some of the facts we are already acquainted with, relating to the proper motion of the stars. And first let me observe, that the rules of philosophizing direct us to refer all phenomena to as few and simple principles as are sufficient to explain them. Thus, for instance, we see the stars and planets rise and set every day: now, as it is much more simple to admit the earth to turn once in 24 hours, than to suppose every single star to revolve round the earth in that time, we very justly ascribe a diurnal motion to the earth; but yet, since we find that the planets do not every night exactly retain their relative places among the stars, we next admit that such deviations from the law, which all the rest seem to obey, are owing to a proper motion of their own. To apply this to the solar system.—Astronomers have already observed what they call a proper motion in several of the fixed stars, and the same may be supposed of them all. We ought, therefore, to resolve that which is common to all the stars, which are found to have what has been called a proper motion, into a single real motion of the solar system, as far as that will answer the known facts, and only to attribute to the proper motion of each particular star the deviations from the general law the stars seem to follow in those movements.

By DR. MASKELYNE'S account of the proper motion of some principal stars,[a] we find that Sirius, Castor, Procyon, Pollux, Regulus, Arcturus, and α Aquilæ, appear to have respectively the following proper motions in right ascension: $-0''\cdot 63$; $-0''\cdot 28$; $-0''\cdot 80$; $-0''\cdot 93$; $-0''\cdot 41$; $-1''\cdot 40$; and $+0''\cdot 57$; and two of them, Sirius and Arcturus, in declination, *viz.* $1''\cdot 20$ and $2''\cdot 01$, both southward. Let fig. 4 represent an equatorial zone, with the above mentioned stars referred to it, according to their respective right ascensions, having the solar system in its center. Assume the direction AB from a point somewhere not far from the 77th degree of right ascension to its opposite 257th degree, and suppose the sun to move in that direction from S towards B; then will that one motion answer that of all the stars together: for if the supposition be true, Arcturus, Regulus, Pollux, Procyon, Castor, and Sirius, should appear to decrease in right ascension, while α Aquilæ, on the contrary, should appear to increase. Moreover, suppose the sun to ascend at the same time in the same direction towards some point in the northern hemisphere, for instance, towards the constellation of Hercules; then will also the observed change of declination of Sirius and Arcturus be resolved into the single motion of the solar system. I am well aware of the many yet remaining difficulties, such as the correspondence of the exact quantity of each star's observed proper motion with the quantity that will be assigned to it by this hypothesis; but we ought to remember, that the very different and still unknown relative distances of the fixed stars must, for a good while yet, leave us in the dark about the particular and strict application of the theory; and that any deviation from it may easily be accounted for by the still unknown *real* proper motion of the stars: for if the solar system have the motion I ascribe to it, then what astronomers have already observed concerning the change of place of the stars, and have called their proper

---

[a] *Astronomical Observations made at the Royal Observatory at Greenwich.*

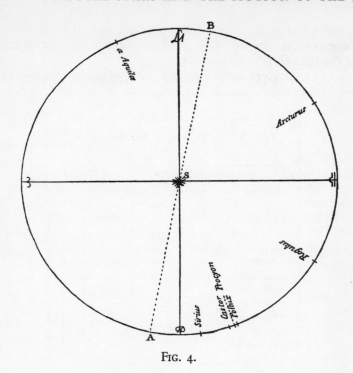

FIG. 4.

motion, will become only an *apparent* motion; and it will still be left to future observations to point out, by the deviations from the general law which the stars will follow in those apparent motions, what may be their real proper motions as well as relative distances. But lest I should be censured for admitting so new and capital a motion upon too slight a foundation, I must observe, that the concurrence of those seven principal stars cannot but give some value to an hypothesis that will simplify the celestial motions in general. We know that the sun, at the distance of a fixed star, would appear like one of them; and from analogy we conclude the stars to be suns. Now, since the apparent motions of these seven stars may be accounted for, either by supposing them to move just in the manner they appear to do, or else by supposing the sun alone to have a motion in a direction, somehow not far from that which I have assigned to it, I think we are no more authorised to suppose the sun at rest than we should be to deny the diurnal motion of the earth, except in this respect, that the proofs of the latter are very numerous, whereas the former rests only on a few though capital testimonies. But to proceed: I have only

49

mentioned the motions of those seven principal stars, as being the most noticed and best ascertained of all; I will now adduce a farther confirmation of the same from other stars.

M. DE LA LANDE gives us the following table of the proper motion of 12 stars, both in right ascension and declination, in 50 years.[a]

| Etoiles. | Chang. d'asc. droite. | | Chang. de déclinaison. | |
|---|---|---|---|---|
| | $'$ | $''$ | $'$ | $''$ |
| Arcturus | −1 | 11 | −1 | 55 |
| Sirius | − | 37 | − | 52 |
| $\beta$ Cygni | − | 3 | + | 49 |
| Procyon | − | 33 | − | 47 |
| $\varepsilon$ Cygni | + | 20 | + | 34 |
| $\gamma$ Arietis | − | 14 | − | 29 |
| $\gamma$ Gemin. | − | 8 | − | 24 |
| Aldébaran | + | 3 | − | 18 |
| $\beta$ Gemin. | − | 48 | − | 16 |
| $\gamma$ Piscium | + | 53 | + | 7 |
| $\alpha$ Aquilæ | + | 32 | − | 4 |
| $\alpha$ Gemin. | − | 24 | − | 1 |

Fig. 5 represents them projected on the plane of the equator. They are all in the northern hemisphere, except Sirius, which must be supposed to be viewed in the concave part of the opposite half of the globe, while the rest are drawn on the convex surface. Regulus being added to that number, and Castor being double, we have 14 stars. Every star's motion, except Regulus, is assigned in declination as well as in right ascension, so that we have no less than 27 motions given to account for. Now, by assuming a point somewhere near $\lambda$ Herculis, and supposing the sun to have a proper motion towards that part of the heaven, we shall satisfy 22 of these motions.[b] For $\beta$ Cygni, $\alpha$ Aquilæ, $\varepsilon$ Cygni, $\gamma$ Piscium, $\gamma$ Arietis, and Aldebaran, ought, upon the supposed motion of the sun, to have an apparent progression, according to the hour circle XVIII, XIX, XX, &c. or to increase in right ascension, while Arcturus, Regulus, the two stars

[a] *Ast.* par M. DE LA LANDE, tom. IV. p. 685.

[b] [In his original version, Herschel thought that he could account satisfactorily for the change in declination of $\beta$ and $\varepsilon$ Cygni, so satisfying twenty-four out of the twenty-seven motions and leaving only three "deviations".]

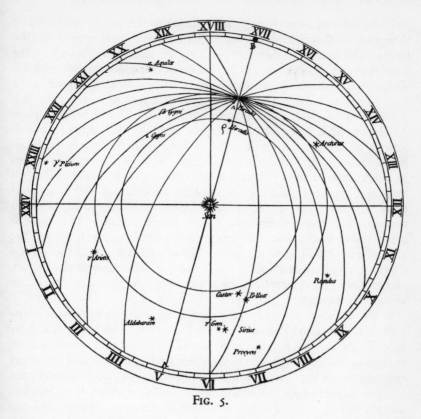

FIG. 5.

of α Geminorum, Pollux, Procyon, Sirius, and γ Geminorum, should apparently go back in the order XVI, XV, XIV, &c. of the hour circle, so as to decrease in right ascension; but according to M. DE LA LANDE's table, excepting β Cygni and γ Arietis, all these motions really take place. With regard to the change of declination, we see that every star in the table should go towards the south;[a] and here we find but three exceptions in β and ε Cygni, and γ Piscium; so that upon the whole we have but five deviations out of 27 known motions which this hypothesis will not account for. And these exceptions must be resolved into the real proper motion of the stars.

[a] [This sentence originally read: "With regard to the change of declination, we see that β and ε Cygni should go towards the north pole as lying between the Pole and the point towards which the sun is supposed to move; and that all the rest ought to go towards the south, or encrease their n[orth] polar distance."]

There are also some very striking circumstances in the quantities of these motions that deserve our notice. First, Arcturus and Sirius being the largest of the stars, and therefore probably the nearest, ought to have the most apparent motion, both in right ascension and declination, which is agreeable to observation, as we find by the table. Next, in regard to the right ascension only, Arcturus being better situated to shew its motion, by theorem 2 (p. 46), ought to have it much larger, which we find it has. Aldebaran, both badly situated and considerably smaller than the two former, by the same theorem ought to shew but little motion. Procyon, better situated than Sirius, though not quite so large, should have almost as much motion; for by the third theorem, on supposing it farther off because it appears smaller, the effect of the sun's motion will be lessened upon it; whereas, on the other hand, by the second theorem, its better situation will partly compensate for its greater distance. This again is conformable to the table. $\varepsilon$ Cygni very favourably situated, though but a small star, should shew it considerably as well as $\alpha$ Aquilæ; whereas $\beta$ Cygni should have but little motion: and $\gamma$ Pisicum, best situated of all, should have a great increase of right ascension, and these deductions also agree with the table.

In the last place, a very striking agreement with the hypothesis is displayed in Castor and Pollux. They are both pretty well situated, and we accordingly find that Pollux, for the size of the star, shews as much motion in right ascension as we could expect; but it is remarkable, and seemingly contrary to our hypothesis, that Castor, equally well placed, shews by the table no more than one half of the motion of Pollux. Now, if we recollect that the former is a double star, consisting of two stars not much different in size, we can allow but about half the light to each of them, which affords a strong presumption of their being at a greater distance, and therefore their partial systematical parallax, by the third theorem, ought to be so much less than that of Pollux, which agrees wonderfully with observation.[a] Not to mention the great difficulty in which we should be involved,

[a] If the light of Castor was exactly equal to that of Pollux, and the two stars, which make up the former star, were perfectly of the same size, we might, on that account, suppose the distance of Castor from us to be to that of Pollux as $\sqrt{2} : 1$; but Castor is in fact something less bright; and this consideration, added to the former, will make it probable enough that its distance may perhaps be double that of Pollux. [This note was added after the paper was read. Maskelyne suggested in a letter of 15 March 1783, that the stars of Castor "may belong to a particular system, which of course would all move together". Herschel in his reply of 17 March agreed, but argued that until this was proved to be so the evidence added to the probabilities in favour of his case.]

were we to suppose the motion of Castor to be really in the star: for how extraordinary must appear the concurrence, that two stars, namely those that make up this apparently single star, should both have a proper motion so exactly alike, that in all our observations hitherto they have not been found to disagree a single second, either in right ascension or declination, for fifty years together! Does not this seem strongly to point out the common cause, the motion of the solar system?

With respect to the change of declination I would observe, that the point of λ Herculis, which in fig. 5 is assumed as the Apex[a] of the solar motion is not perhaps the best selected. A somewhat more northern situation may agree better with the changes of declination of Arcturus and Sirius, which capital stars may perhaps be the most proper to lead us in this hypothesis; but as we should be guided by facts in researches of this nature, it may be as well to expect the assistance of future observations before we are too particular in determining this point.[b]

It may be expected I should also mention something concerning the quantity of the solar motion; but here I can only offer a few distant hints. From the annual parallax of the fixed stars, which, from my own observations, I find much less than it has hitherto been proved to be, we may certainly admit (without entering into a subject which I reserve for a future opportunity) that the diameter of the earth's orbit, at the distance of Sirius or Arcturus, would not nearly subtend an angle of one second; but the apparent motion of Arcturus, if owing to a translation of the solar system, amounts to no less than $2''{\cdot}7$ a year, as will appear if we compound the two motions of $1'\ 11''$ in right ascension, and $1'\ 55''$ in declination, into one single motion, and reduce it to an annual quantity. Hence we may in a general way estimate, that the solar motion can certainly not be less than that which the earth has in her annual orbit.

I have now only to add, that it is to be expected future observations will soon throw more light upon this interesting subject, and either fully

[a] I use the term Apex here to denote that point of fig. 5, wherein all great circles, drawn through the supposed direction of the motion of the solar system, intersect, and which, in other stereographic projections, is generally a pole, either of the ecliptic or equator. As this point is the northern or elevated hemisphere, the sun, by tending to it, may be said to ascend, and the term Apex may perhaps not be an improper one.

[b] From the additional testimony of other capital stars considered in the postscript [not reproduced] it now appears, that the point of λ Herculis is probably as well chosen as any we can fix upon in that part of the heavens. [Footnote added after the paper was read. The original version of Herschel's text of this passage is reproduced at the end of the paper.]

establish or overturn the hypothesis of the motion of the whole solar system. To this end I have already begun a series of observation upon several zones of double stars; and should the result of them be against these conjectures, I shall be the first to endeavour to point out the fallacy of them.

Datchet near Windsor,
Feb. 1, 1783.

[Instead of as above, p. 44, l. 20 to p. 45, l. 1, Herschel's paper as submitted read: " . . . less in motion. May not a star which is lost be looked upon as one whose proper motion has carried it directly out of our sight? A new one which appears may be such a one whose proper motion brings it immediately into our view: A star which increases in magnitude and changes its place by slow degrees, may be one which moves in an oblique direction towards us: A gradually vanishing star, with change of place, may be that which moves obliquely from us: And a star that changes its place without altering its magnitude may be such a one whose motion is at rectangles to a line drawn from the Sun to that star. Now if observations continually point out such *changes in the apparent magnitudes and reciprocal distances of the stars* [italics not in original] who can hesitate to pronounce their proper motions? And if the proper motion. . . ."

Instead of as above, p. 53, lines 8–15, Herschel's paper as submitted read: "If the change in declination of $\beta$ & $\varepsilon$ Cygni be thrown on their own proper motion, rather than that of the Solar-System, we shall be able to make other quantities agree much better with observation, by supposing the Sun to move towards a more nothern star, such as $\varrho$ Herculis. It seems the motion of Arcturus and Sirius is too great to permit the Apex to lie so low as either $\lambda$ or the 51st Herculis. If it were raised to the parallel of the 50th of the same constellation, we should only throw out $\beta$ Cygni, which is a star from other reasons much to be suspected of a real proper motion; but even this elevation would hardly suffice: I would rather consider Arcturus and Sirius as the leading marks to regulate that point. It can not be said that I act arbitrarily in assigning to $\varepsilon$ and $\beta$ Cygni motions at pleasure, as best suits my hypothesis; for since proper motions have actually been observed, if they are not to be accounted for from that of the Sun, they must needs be in the stars themselves; and as in this hypothesis I would intirely be directed by facts, it is highly proper, where contrary motions appear, to lean to the side which has the strongest arguments in its favour."]

Even today there is an uncertainty of several degrees in estimates of the direction of solar motion, but $\lambda$ Herculis is not far from the truth. It was a well-judged conclusion drawn from the minimum of data by straightforward inspection and calculation, and in fair agreement with the direction found by Prévost the same year and very close indeed to the direction given by Klügel in 1789.

Herschel himself returned to the problem soon after completing the sweeps for nebulæ,[42] and he published two closely related papers, the first[43] in 1805 in which he recalculated the direction of solar motion and the second[44] in the following year in which he estimated its speed. In their quantitative results, these papers are less convincing, coming as they did at a time when the data were too cumbersome for straightforward treatment yet insufficient for statistical analysis; their interest lies rather in the considerations that directed Herschel's thinking at the turning-points of his argument.

The 1805 paper appears innocent enough. Instead of exploiting the full wealth of information given in Maskelyne's table of thirty-six proper motions of stars he selected six bright stars (chosen for reasons we shall discuss below) and by graphical methods arrived at a direction for the solar motion which would reduce to a minimum the residual proper motions of these six stars. His result, though not wildly false, is less accurate than that of his earlier paper.

In studying the speed of the solar motion the following year, on the other hand, Herschel took into account the full thirty-six proper motions given in Maskelyne's table. This table gave the yearly angular shift of these stars, and to convert these figures into velocities it was necessary for him to know the distances of these stars (as also to assume for argument's sake that they were moving at right angles to the line of sight). These distances he derived by a strict application of the 'brightness equals nearness' principle to estimates of comparative brightnesses, reckoning Rigel for example to be 1·35 times farther than Sirius, whereas we know it is 540 light-years away compared with Sirius's 8·7. This done, he found "that 17 out of the 21 stars, whose motions are directed towards the north, are crowded together into a compass of little more than 76½ degrees",[45] this angle including the direction he had assigned to the Sun.

The reader might strongly have objected at this stage that

when the solar motion had been allowed for, the residual velocities (due to the motion of the stars themselves) would be more numerous and even more closely clustered than the apparent ones; and that since solar motion had been introduced in the first place to eliminate motions, not to increase them and accentuate existing patterns among them, some quite different direction for solar motion ought to be chosen. Herschel saw this objection perfectly well. "The chief object in view," he had written in 1805, "when a solar motion was proposed to be deduced from observations of the proper motions of stars, was to take away many of these motions by investing the sun with a contrary one. But the solar motion, when its existence has been proved, will reveal so many concealed real motions, that we shall have a greater sum of them than it would be necessary to admit, if the sun were at rest."[46] And he restated this difficulty in the 1806 paper after calculating the residual velocities:

> Indeed, if we except only ten of the stars, all the rest appear to be actuated by the same influence, and like faithful companions of the sun, to join in directing their motions towards a similarly situated part of the heavens. This singularity is too marked not to deserve an examination; for unless a cause for such particular directions can be shown to exist, I do not see how we can reconcile them with a certain equal distribution of situations, quantities, and motions, which our present investigation seems to demand.[47]

There was a simple and obvious remedy, namely, to recalculate the direction of solar motion on the basis of a different set of six stars—and in fact the selection of the original six is curious. In the 1806 paper Herschel gave the first eight stars in order of brightness as Sirius, Arcturus, Capella, Lyra, Rigel and Betelgeuse (equal), Procyon and Aldebaran (equal); and likewise in his earlier catalogues of comparative brightnesses of stars he had noted that Rigel and Betelgeuse were brighter than Procyon.[48] Yet in selecting six "brightest" or "principal" stars he had omitted from these eight Rigel and Betelgeuse. Why?

At the beginning of the 1805 paper, Herschel tells us that he plotted on a globe the intersections of the proper motions of Maskelyne's thirty-six stars, and "I find no less than ten that are made by stars of the first magnitude, in a very limited part of the heavens, about the constellation of Hercules."[49] Now these ten intersections are all associated with the six stars he later selected. In other words, the choice of these six was sure to direct the solar motion towards Hercules—a direction desirable not so much for consistency with his 1783 paper, for he drew attention to the *difference* between his former and his present estimates, but for the solution of fundamental problems arising from the table of proper velocities of stars which he had derived from Maskelyne's list.

This table presented him with results which could be interpreted in various ways, all implying breakdowns in uniformity (and while, as he was willing to admit, "it may be objected that our idea of the congruence or harmony of the celestial motions can be no criterion of their real fitness and quantity",[50] a resistance to unnecessary increases in complexity is surely a mark of a scientific mind). In themselves, and before any allowance was made for the Sun's motion, the velocities in the table were clustered in direction, as we have already seen, *and* they varied sharply in quantity, with many of the brightest stars having the lowest speeds. Faced with this, Herschel could have doubted the 'brightness equals nearness' principle on which the computations were based, but the effect of this would have been to bring his investigation to an end; he could have chosen the solar velocity so as to produce a greater scattering of direction, at the expense of increasing the already wide disparities in speed; or he could have decreased the differences in speed at the expense of accentuating further the clustering of the directions.

In fact, he chose the last course: for whereas he was unhappy about the wide variations in speeds, he could see his way to explaining the clustering in directions. Had he not foreseen this very possibility back in 1783 when writing the postscript to his paper in the light of Michell's work on star systems? He had pointed out there that "the second table contains those stars whose motions cannot be accounted for by my hypothesis, and must therefore be ascribed to a real motion in the stars themselves, or to some *still more hidden* cause of a *still remoter* parallax"[51] (Herschel's italics), and in a long footnote he had referred to Michell's work and suggested that the study of proper motions might offer clues to "which stars may possibly belong to ours, and which to other systems". If, then, the Sun and neighbouring stars were moving together under some powerful force of attraction—perhaps moving in orbit like the planets round the Sun—the neighbouring stars would *appear* to be moving slowly; but when allowance was made for the motion of the Sun it would be realized that these stars were in fact keeping pace with the Sun, moving with similar speed and direction.

What the Sun's speed was, Herschel determined in a rather arbitrary fashion, justified on the grounds that his value duly slowed down the fastest stars and speeded up the slowest, so that the greatest and least speeds differed by only a factor of $7\frac{1}{2}$ in place of the previous 24; and it gave the Sun middle position when the stars were ranked in order of their speeds. To attempt to compare it with modern values would be to endow Herschel's reasoning with a methodical precision it never attained. "His arguments are very ingenious," wrote Professor John Brinkley of Dublin University, "but there is necessarily so much hypothetical in them, that the mind cannot feel much confidence in his conclusion."[52]

What, one wonders, would Herschel have done if Maskelyne's list had included the proper motion of 61 Cygni: for its very large motion, multiplied by the distance suggested by the faintness of the star, would have resulted in a supposed velocity many times greater than of any other star in Herschel's table. This fact would necessarily have dominated Herschel's considerations, but would it have forced him to accept the seemingly unavoidable conclusion that he must abandon the rigorous application of the 'brightness equals nearness' principle? One suspects not.

By this time, however, other astronomers were becoming doubtful whether any pattern was in fact to be found among the growing number of known proper motions. Baily in 1831 summed up the general opinion when he said:

The additional information, however, which we have subsequently obtained on this subject, and the discovery of proper motions, in many of the stars, much greater in amount than any which he [Herschel] contemplated, do not appear to confirm this theory. And M. Bessel, who has investigated this subject [in 1818] with his usual care and ability, states that many of the stars indicate a point in the heavens very remote from the one alluded to by Sir William Herschel: and that, in fact, there is no one point in particular, towards which he can discover any such tendency.[53]

But then in 1837 Argelander published an analysis based on the proper motions of no less than three hundred and ninety stars which showed after all that there was indeed a point and that it was not far from Herschel's 1783 position. Confirmation of this boosted Herschel's reputation until we find the 1805 paper compared to Newton's *Principia* "for sustained reflection and high philosophic thought"![54] Fickle indeed is the Muse of History.

# Chapter Three

# The Construction of the Heavens: the first synthesis

THE first telescopic observations of the milky patches to be found in various parts of the sky had been made in the early years of the seventeenth century, and as the number of known 'nebulæ' increased so too did interest in the problem of whether these nebulæ were in fact distant clusters of stars whose individual light was too faint to be detected, or whether they were luminous clouds of a nature previously unknown.

Both views had their champions. In an unsigned article in the *Philosophical Transactions* for 1716, the author (possibly Halley) argued that nebulæ "in reality are nothing else but the Light coming from an extraordinary great Space in the Ether; through which a lucid *Medium* is diffused, that shines with its own proper Lustre".[1] Michell, on the other hand, in his 1767 paper suggested that "Those stars, which are surrounded with nebulae, are probably only very great stars, which, on account of their superior magnitude, are singly visible, whilst the others, which compose the remaining parts of the same system, are so small as to escape our sight. And those nebulæ, in which we can discover either none, or only a few stars, even with the assistance of the best telescopes, are probably systems, that are still more distant than the rest."[2] And after considering how the Sun and its neighbours might appear to a spectator in the Pleiades, he remarked: "This may serve to show us that those nebulæ, in which we cannot distinguish any stars, may yet reasonably be supposed to consist of stars, though too far distant to be singly visible; since this would be the case with our own system, seen from as great a distance as we may well suppose those nebulæ to be from us, if we judge of it from the magnitude of this visible area which they occupy in the heavens."[3]

In his early years as an astronomer, Herschel had read Smith's account of the great nebula in Orion, and the observations he made of it in 1774 appear at the beginning of his first astronomical journal. These long-standing interests were reawakened in December 1781, when Watson presented him[4] with a "Catalogue des Nébuleuses et des amas d'Étoiles" published by Charles Messier in the *Connoissance des Temps* for 1783. Here was an opportunity for Herschel's 20-foot telescope, so much superior to those at Messier's disposal, to show its power. Sure enough, he "saw, with the greatest pleasure, that most of the nebulæ . . . yielded to the force of my light and power, and were resolved into stars" (below, p. 73). What more natural than to suppose that *all* these alleged nebulæ were no more than distant clusters?—for in this way all the appearances could be explained (or, in the term of an earlier period, 'saved') without the need to postulate the novelty of a luminous fluid.

The nebulæ of Messier in fact include gaseous clouds in our own Galaxy which cannot be resolved into stars, as well as external galaxies whose stars can be discerned, if at all, only with the aid of photography (below, pp. 73-4, notes). In other words, Herschel's hypothesis was false. But it would not easily be disproved for two reasons. First, it 'saved the appearances' easily—if anything, too easily, for almost any unresolved nebula could be explained away as a distant cluster resolvable only by a more powerful telescope. Secondly, observations

intended to test it could be misleading, for as Herschel strained
his eyes and tried to detect the presence of stars in a nebula,
operating at and beyond the limits even of his great skill as an
observer, he sometimes persuaded himself he could see what
his mind told him to expect. By 1784 he was writing to Bode
that he had resolved "presque toutes les nebuleuses"[5] of Messier's
catalogue. "A mottled kind of nebulosity" suggested to him,
and more than suggested, the presence of stars. M31, for example,
the great nebula in Andromeda, is of course a galaxy similar to
our own, but its individual stars are readily detectable only by
photography and certainly could not be seen visually in any
telescope that Herschel possessed. Yet he included it in his list
of Messier nebulæ which "have either plainly appeared to be
nothing but stars, or at least to contain stars, and to shew every
other indication of consisting of them entirely" (below, p. 73;
cf. p. 107). In 1811, on the other hand, when he no longer
believed all nebulæ to be star clusters, he described it as "not
resolvable".[6]

Characteristically, Herschel decided that Messier's catalogue,
increased to a total of one hundred and three nebulæ and star
clusters in the *Connoissance des Temps* for 1784, was altogether
inadequate, and that he must play the natural historian and collect many specimens. Accordingly, in October 1783, he began
his twenty years of sweeping for nebulæ with his new and larger
20-foot reflector. "This will be a work of some years," he
wrote to a friend, "but it is, to me, so far from laborious, that
it is attended with the utmost delight."[7] The creative scientist
must be permitted convictions that go beyond the evidence,
and in a paper published in January 1785, Herschel sometimes
equates nebulæ with star clusters (below, pp. 83-4). But it
speaks well for his integrity as an observer that he lists at the end
of the paper what he called 'planetary nebulæ', bodies "that from
their singular appearance leave me almost in doubt where to
class them" (below, p. 103); and some weeks later, in writing
to the French astronomer Lalande, he described them as "des

corps celestes dont nous n'avons pas encore d'idée bien claire & qui sont peut-être d'un genre tout à fait different de ce que nous connoissons des les cieux".[8] Planetary nebulæ (the misleading term is still retained today) consist of a sphere or shell of gas surrounding a central star which may be invisible to direct observation but is often conspicuous on photographs; and in the end it was the unmistakable association of one such nebula with the central star that finally persuaded Herschel to abandon his hypothesis (below, pp. 119-29).

During the early years of sweeping for nebulæ, Herschel published three papers on the construction of the heavens (reproduced below), in 1784, 1785, and 1789 respectively. One important topic which, with regrettably typical lack of organization, he touches on twice in the 1784 paper but only investigates fully in that of 1785, is the *structure* of our Galaxy. The general shape of the Milky Way as it appears to the observer had of course been known since ancient times, and Galileo's telescope had revealed many more stars than could be detected by the naked eye. The major step in interpretation had come in 1750 with the publication of Thomas Wright's *An Original Theory or new Hypothesis of the Universe*. Wright, a popular teacher of science and by no means critical in outlook, provided an example of armchair science at its best when he suggested that the Milky Way might be an optical effect rather than an indication of true clustering, and that the stars are actually scattered throughout a region of space which might be thought of as being bounded by two parallel planes. An observer located (on Earth) somewhere between these two planes would then see many stars when he looked out in the direction of the planes, but would see only a few stars, and those mostly near, when he looked out perpendicularly to the planes. Herschel presents a very similar argument in his 1784 paper (below, pp. 75-7); he owned a copy of Wright's book, but it probably came into his possession at a later date.[a]

[a] For a discussion of this question, see below pp. 115-6.

The suggestion was extremely plausible, but before Herschel appeared on the scene nothing further had been done. Indeed, how could one advance beyond this qualitative description of Wright's and arrive at some quantitative knowledge of the 'geography' of the Galaxy? Herschel saw a way of answering this question. As we have seen, he was prone to assume uniformities in the heavens whenever the evidence allowed, and he realized that by making two assumptions he could succeed in producing a map of the Galaxy. These assumptions were, first (adapting Halley's model), that throughout the space occupied by the Galaxy the stars are distributed (more or less) uniformly, and, second, that his telescopes were able to penetrate to the edges of the Galaxy in all directions. Both assumptions, he later realized, were hopelessly false. As he admitted in 1817 (below, pp. 185–6), his telescopes could not "fathom" the Milky Way, while the 'star-gages' "which on a supposition of an equality of scattering were looked upon as gages of distance, . . . in fact, relate more immediately to the scattering of the stars"[9] (compare below, p. 90). But it was a remarkable achievement to follow so unlikely a programme through to a conclusion and in so doing to demonstrate the latent possibilities of stellar statistics.

Herschel hints at his technique of 'star-gages' in the 1784 paper (below, pp. 77–9), but he applies it only in 1785 (below, pp. 87–96). He argues that when he looks through his telescope he sees the stars in a cone of space, vertex at the observer. By the second assumption, he sees *all* the stars in that cone, right up to the edge of the Galaxy. By the first assumption, these stars are uniformly distributed throughout the cone as far as the edge of the Galaxy, so that merely by counting stars and applying a simple formula it is possible to determine the distance to the edge of the Galaxy in that particular direction. In his 1785 paper, the gages, the formulæ, the conversion table to translate gages into distances, and a drawing of a cross-section of the Galaxy, are all set out.

It is significant that for some of the gages corresponding to quite short distances, Herschel expressly comments, "Most of the stars extremely small." This is the case, for example, with his third gage (below, p. 88), sandwiched though it is between gages corresponding to larger distances. In other words, the results from the gages are sometimes in direct contradiction to the 'brightness equals nearness' principle—yet another example of Herschel's ability to close his eyes to inconvenient facts.[10]

Another important feature of the 1784 paper is Herschel's announcement that 'nebulæ' are not scattered at random across the sky but are dense in some directions and rare in others (below, p. 75). As we now know, this effect is partly due to obscuring dust which impedes observation in the plane of our Galaxy but which allows us to see clearly in the direction of the poles of the Galaxy, and partly to genuine clustering among external galaxies. Both these factors are at work in, for example, the direction of Coma Berenices, mentioned by Herschel (below, pp. 81–2), which is both far from the plane of the Galaxy and contains (among others) the Virgo cluster of galaxies and the Coma Berenices cluster.

Meanwhile the rapidly growing list of nebulæ and star clusters discovered by Herschel was raising problems of its own: in particular, how were these hundreds of objects to be catalogued? Herschel's own brief description of star clusters naturally emphasized the *degree* of clustering they exhibited, and he later classified them as "very compressed and rich", "pretty much compressed", or "coarsely scattered". Now the very term 'cluster' suggested that attractive powers were at work, and so what was more natural than to interpret the degree of clustering as an index of the length of *time* during which attractive powers had been forming the cluster? Of the nebulæ and star clusters, then, some are older than others, some more distant than others. To explore this further, Herschel announced in his 1785 paper, that he will "take the subject from a point of view at a considerable distance both of space and of time" (below, p. 83).

He begins by insisting on the equal importance of observations and interpretations, citing Cartesian vortices as a warning of the fate awaiting theories built on insufficient evidence. His example is an interesting one. Descartes, in his *Le Monde* and *Principia Philosophiae*, seeks to explain the movement of the planets about the Sun as part of a vortex or general circulation of matter through the region of the solar system; this vortex in turn is explained as typical of what *must* happen in any world God creates: if God set a world in motion in arbitrary fashion, under stated laws of motion which depend directly upon the immutability of God, the matter of the world *must* ultimately settle down into a series of such vortices. In other words, Descartes explains what we see as inevitably coming to be out of a more primitive arrangement of matter in motion, the process working itself out under known laws.

This limited view of an evolutionary process taking place in the world—limited, because an essentially stable situation is eventually reached—was sharply attacked by Newton. In an illuminating passage in Query 31 of his *Opticks*, he writes:

> Now by the help of these Principles [of Motion], all material Things seem to have been composed of the hard and solid Particles above-mention'd, variously associated in the first Creation by the Counsel of an intelligent Agent. For it became him who created them to set them in order. And if he did so, it's unphilosophical to seek for any other Origin of the World, or to pretend that it might arise out of a Chaos by the mere Laws of Nature. . . . Blind fate could never make all the Planets move one and the same way in Orbs concentrick, some inconsiderable Irregularities excepted, which may have arisen from the mutual Actions of Comets and Planets upon one another, and which will be apt to increase, till this System want a Reformation.[11]

Newton was, like Descartes and many others of the period, very much under the influence of the mechanical philosophy, which saw matter in motion as the basic ingredient of scientific explanation. The complexities of clockwork machinery seemed particularly instructive at this time, and God was assigned the role of master clockmaker. Unlike Descartes, Newton did not have any profound interest in living things to offset the essentially static conception of the world suggested by the clockwork model, and the planetary system with its uniformities argued for him the finished product of the clockmaker. As we have already seen, so much was he in the grip of this image of the world that even when the planetary system threatened to prove unstable under the law of gravitation Newton preferred to invoke a direct intervention of God to 'reform' the system rather than allow the 'clock' to fragment, and his spokesman Samuel Clarke clung to this position under repeated attack from Leibnitz.[12] As Laplace was later to show, Newton was mistaken in thinking the planetary system unstable; had he realized this, we might perhaps have failed to realize the extent of his commitment to the clockwork model.

The eighteenth century, especially in France, saw a major shift in the climate of opinion. The idea of progress in human affairs became popular and encouraged in one sphere at least the view that the future would be significantly different from the past. In various branches of science the idea of a stable order, whether in the machinery of the heavens or in the fixed sovereign order of nature among living things, was eroded and gradually replaced. At the middle of the century, for example, Buffon[13] took the uniformities among the motions of the planets not as proof of a Designer but as evidence of their common origin, which he believed to have been a collision of the Sun with a comet. In 1778, talking now not in terms of the six thousand years since the creation which Newton and many of his contemporaries had calculated on the basis of a Fundamentalist interpretation of Old Testament chronology but in epochs of tens of thousands of years, Buffon sketched[14] the subsequent development of the Earth from its molten state immediately following the collision to the appearance of animals and finally man. By the end of the century biological evolution was receiving its first full expression at the hands of Lamarck, and Earth history was past its infancy—though, as we shall see, many still lacked the confidence to infer change from static evidence.

Herschel produced in his lifetime two great syntheses embodying theories of what we might term the 'evolution' of nebulæ and star clusters. Of these, the first was outlined in the 1785 paper, the introduction to his second catalogue of nebulæ and star clusters published in 1789 being an *apologia* setting out persuasively the processes by which he reached—or, at least, rationalized—his conclusions. For Herschel at this period, unresolved nebulae differed importantly from star clusters in being more distant—rather than being younger, as in many cases he was later to think—and so the time factor had not yet assumed its later overriding importance. In addition he had recently discovered the concentrations of nebulæ in certain parts of the sky, and these too had to be explained. His theory, therefore, embraces the development of star systems spatially as well as temporally.

Herschel knew perfectly well that on a human time-scale a nebula can change but slowly,[a] and that he must be satisfied with outlining a hypothetical process of development that would—if found in Nature—lead to nebulæ and clusters similar to those (virtually static) objects he had observed. He chose to start with an initially more or less uniform distribution of stars, and then to ask himself how this system might develop under the action of gravitational attraction or other such forces. Similar almost-uniform distributions had been canvassed by others besides Halley, but usually in connexion with a universe in near-equilibrium. For Herschel this primitive uniformity is soon irretrievably lost, but its ghost lives on as the standard by

[a] Although it was mistakenly believed by many (including Herschel) that major changes had taken place in the great nebula in Orion. *Cf.* Messier in *Connoissance des Temps* for 1783, p. 225; letter of Schroeter to Herschel, December 1797, and Herschel's comments; and Herschel's own observations, Dreyer, II, 654-7, and *Phil. Trans.*, CI (1811), 320-5=Dreyer, II, 488-91. For the implications of these changes, see below, p. 117.

which to assess the present situation. He similarly retains something of the earlier uniformities when in the 1789 paper in spite of his preoccupation with clustering—that is, with non-uniformity—he sees among these very clusters uniformities such as we find among the members of a species of plant or animal (below, p. 113-4).

Needless to say, with so vague a statement of the problem Herschel has little difficulty in imagining how irregularities in the original distribution of stars could have given rise to the nebulæ and star clusters he has observed: his achievement is more brilliant in conception than in execution. But he does recognize with remarkable composure that this star system of ours is only one among many such systems and of no special significance—a view found in philosophical works of the eighteenth century but only now supported by evidence. It is sometimes assumed today that a progressive dethroning of Man has been continuously under way from Copernicus via Darwin and Freud; but Herschel's assertion that there are many galaxies comparable to our own was in considerable doubt even at the beginning of the present century, and was only put beyond dispute by E. P. Hubble as recently as 1923-4. Yet it must be admitted that Herschel was greatly helped by his hopeless underestimate of the dimensions of the Galaxy, while at the same time his belief that all nebulæ, even when as extensive as that of Orion, were distant star systems gave him confidence in the great size of systems external to our own Galaxy (below, p. 100). This confidence diminished when he recognized the existence of "true nebulosity", so that in the end he is uncertain (below, p. 156) whether even the impressive galaxy M31, the Andromeda nebula, is a distant star system or near-by nebulosity. Equally, his recognition that our Galaxy was for his telescopes actually "fathomless" and therefore of unknown extent made it difficult for him then to compare it with known finite objects. It is not surprising, then, that his later work on the structure of the heavens lacks the sureness of touch of his earlier writings.

In fact, astronomers and historians have argued ever since as to whether or not Herschel actually abandoned his view of the Galaxy as one of many "island" star systems. It seems most likely that he did not, although he certainly came to think of it as of unique size among the known star systems, "the most brilliant, and beyond all comparison the most extensive sidereal system"[15]—a view fully in accord with the evidence at his disposal.

If, Herschel argues in the 1785 paper, our Galaxy is a compound system containing many smaller clusters, then other concentrations of nebulæ (or clusters) are no doubt the sites of other compound systems, present or past. And since he had proved the Galaxy to be flattened in shape, it was natural for him to envisage remnants of other flattened systems as occurring in 'strata'. Now observations had done little to penetrate the mystery of how distant were the nebulæ and star clusters that Herschel had catalogued. In fact, as we now know, they are of several different types and at very different distances. Some are isolated stellar systems, spiral or elliptical, akin to our own Galaxy and separated from us by very great distances. These were known until recently as extra-galactic nebulæ but are now usually termed *galaxies*, *nebula* being reserved for clouds of interstellar gas in our own system; desirable though this may be for the modern astronomer, the unfortunate historian is left with no term vague enough to embrace all of Herschel's objects. Then there are star clusters in our own Galaxy, comprising the galactic (or open) clusters, which are irregular associations of stars lying in the central plane of the Galaxy and so usually appearing close to the Milky Way, and the highly condensed globular clusters, which are spread over a large spherical region surrounding the Galaxy and so may occur in any part of the sky. Finally there are the gaseous or galactic nebulæ, "true nebulosity" in Herschel's language; these are mostly irregular patches of interstellar gas in the plane of the Galaxy, but a few are remnants of the catastrophic explosion of stars, and there are also the imperfectly understood planetary nebulæ consisting of a sphere or shell surrounding a central star. Add to these the near-by constellations of stars on the one hand, and on the other the clusters of galaxies that Herschel had discovered, and it is clear that Herschel is trying to introduce simplicity and order into hopelessly diverse material.

Yet if observations had yielded few clues to distances, theory could suggest a deceptively convincing picture. If the stars had originally been spread out almost uniformly, and had now collected together into nebulæ of various kinds, there was no reason why these nebulæ should be widely separated. Thus the great 'stratum' of nebulæ in the direction of Coma Berenices (actually, as we know, very distant clusters of galaxies, *each* galaxy being comparable to our Galaxy) might, taken as a whole, be similar to our Galaxy and extend towards us so closely as to contain the (near-by) stars of Coma Berenices itself. A union of opposites with a vengeance, yet how plausible!

## Account of some Observations tending to investigate the Construction of the Heavens.[a]

Read June 17, 1784.

IN a former paper I mentioned, that a more powerful instrument was preparing for continuing my reviews of the heavens. The telescope I have lately completed, though far inferior in size to the one I had undertaken to construct when that paper was written, is of the Newtonian form, the object speculum being of 20 feet focal length, and its aperture $18\frac{7}{10}$ inches. The apparatus on which it is mounted is contrived so as at present to confine the instrument to a meridional situation, and by its motions to give the right-ascension and declination of a celestial object in a coarse way; which, however, is sufficiently accurate to point out the place of the object, so that it may be found again. It will not be necessary to enter into a more particular description of the apparatus, since the account I have now the honour of communicating to the Royal Society regards rather the performance of the telescope than its construction.

It would, perhaps, have been more eligible to have waited longer, in

[a] [*Phil. Trans.*, LXXIV (1784), 437–51.]

order to complete the discoveries that seem to lie within the reach of this instrument, and are already, in some respects, pointed out to me by it. By taking more time I should undoubtedly be enabled to speak more confidently of the *interior construction* of the heavens, and its various *nebulous and sidereal strata* (to borrow a term from the natural historian) of which this paper can as yet only give a few outlines, or rather hints. As an apology, however, for this prematurity, it may be said, that the end of all discoveries being communication, we can never be too ready in giving facts and observations, whatever we may be in reasoning upon them.

Hitherto the sidereal heavens have, not inadequately for the purpose designed, been represented by the concave surface of a sphere, in the center of which the eye of an observer might be supposed to be placed. It is true, the various magnitudes of the fixed stars even then plainly suggested to us, and would have better suited the idea of an expanded firmament of three dimensions; but the observations upon which I am now going to enter still farther illustrate and enforce the necessity of considering the heavens in this point of view. In future, therefore, we shall look upon those regions into which we may now penetrate by means of such large telescopes, as a naturalist regards a rich extent of ground or chain of mountains, containing strata variously inclined and directed, as well as consisting of very different materials. A surface of a globe or map, therefore, will but ill delineate the interior parts of the heavens.

It may well be expected, that the great advantage of a large aperture would be most sensibly perceived with all those objects that require much light, such as the very small and immensely distant fixed stars, the very faint nebulæ, the close and compressed clusters of stars, and the remote planets.

On applying the telescope to a part of the *via lactea*, I found that it completely resolved the whole whitish appearance into small stars, which my former telescopes had not light enough to effect. The portion of this extensive tract, which it has hitherto been convenient for me to observe, is that immediately about the hand and club of Orion. The glorious multitude of stars of all possible sizes that presented themselves here to my view was truly astonishing; but, as the dazzling brightness of glittering stars may easily mislead us so far as to estimate their number greater than it really is, I endeavoured to ascertain this point by counting many fields, and computing, from a mean of them, what a certain given portion of the milky way might contain. Among many trials of this sort I found, last January the 18th, that six fields, promiscuously taken, contained 110, 60, 70, 90, 70, and 74 stars each. I then tried to pick out the most vacant place that was to be found in that neighbourhood, and counted 63 stars. A mean of the first six gives 79 stars for each field. Hence, by allowing 15 minutes of a great circle for the diameter of my field of view, we gather, that a belt of 15 degrees long and two broad, or the quantity which I have often seen pass through the field of my telescope in one hour's time, could not well contain less than fifty thousand stars, that were large enough to be distinctly numbered. But, besides these, I suspected at least twice as many more, which, for want of light, I could only see now and then by faint glittering and interrupted glimpses.

The excellent collection of nebulæ and clusters of stars which has lately been given in the *Connoissance des Temps* for 1783 and 1784, leads me next to a subject which, indeed, must open a new view of the heavens. As soon as the first of these volumes came to my hands, I applied my former 20-feet reflector of 12 inches aperture to them; and saw, with the greatest pleasure, that most of the nebulæ, which I had an opportunity of examining in proper situations, yielded to the force of my light and power, and were resolved into stars. For instance, the 2d, 5, 9, 10, 12, 13, 14, 15, 16, 19, 22, 24, 28, 30, 31, 37, 51, 52, 53, 55, 56, 62, 65, 66, 67, 71, 72, 74, 92, all which are said to be nebulæ without stars, have either plainly appeared to be nothing but stars, or at least to contain stars, and to shew every other indication of consisting of them entirely.[a] I have examined them with a careful scrutiny of various powers and light, and generally in the meridian. I should mention, that five of the above, *viz.* the 16th, 24, 37, 52, 67, are called clusters of stars containing nebulosity; but my instrument resolving also that portion of them which is called nebulous into stars of a much smaller size, I have placed them into the above number. To these may be added the 1st, 3d, 27, 33, 57, 79, 81, 82, 101, which in my 7, 10, and 20-feet reflectors shewed a mottled kind of nebulosity, which I shall call resolvable;[b] so that I expect my present telescope will, perhaps, render the stars visible of which I suppose them to be composed. Here I might point

[a] [Of these twenty-nine Messier objects, eighteen are globular clusters and six galactic clusters. (For these and similar terms, see above p. 70.) The successful resolution into stars of many of the globular clusters in Messier's catalogue is a clear indication of the quality of Herschel's telescopes. But Herschel was over-optimistic in expecting M31, 51, 65, 66, and 74 to be visually resolved into stars with a further increase in power: they are galaxies and much too distant for Herschel's instrument to detect individual stars.—D.]

[b] [Of the nine Messier objects only M3 and M79 are globular clusters. The "mottled kind of nebulosity, which I shall call resolvable" misled Herschel in M33, 81, 82, and 101 (galaxies), whilst M1, 27, and 57 are gaseous nebulæ (M1—the "Crab" nebula—the remnant of the supernova of A.D. 1054; M27 and 57, planetary nebulæ).—D.]

out many precautions necessary to be taken with the very best instruments, in order to succeed in the resolution of the most difficult of them; but reserving this at present too extensive subject for a future opportunity, I proceed to speak of the effects of my last instrument with regard to nebulæ.

My present pursuits, as I observed before, requiring this telescope to act as a fixed instrument, I found it not convenient to apply it to any other of the nebulæ in the *Connoissance des Temps* but such as came in turn; nor, indeed, was it necessary to take any particular pains to look for them, it being utterly impossible that any one of them should escape my observation when it passed the field of view of my telescope. The few which I have already had an opportunity of examining, shew plainly that those most excellent French astronomers, MESS. MESSIER and MECHAIN, saw only the more luminous part of their nebulæ; the feeble shape of the remainder, for want of light, escaping their notice. The difference will appear when we compare my observation of the 98th nebula[a] with that in the *Connoissance des Temps* for 1784, which runs thus: "Nébuleuse sans étoile, d'une lumière extrêmement foible, au dessus de l'aile boréale de la Vierge, sur le parallèle et près de l'étoile N° 6, cinquième grandeur, de la chevelure de Bérénice, suivant FLAMSTEED. M. MECHAIN la vit le 15 Mars, 1781." My observation of the 30th of December, 1783, is thus: A large, extended, fine nebula. Its situation shews it to be M. MESSIER's 98th; but from the description it appears, that that gentleman has not seen the whole of it, for its feeble branches extend above a quarter of a degree, of which no notice is taken. Near the middle of it are a few stars visible, and more suspected. My field of view will not quite take in the whole nebula. See fig. 1, Plate I. Again, N° 53,[b] "Nébuleuse sans étoiles, decouverte au-dessous et près de la chevelure de Bérénice, à peu de distance de l'étoile quarante-deuxieme de cette constellation, suivant FLAMSTEED. Cette nébuleuse est ronde et apparente, &c." My observation of the 170th Sweep runs thus: A cluster of very close stars; one of the most beautiful objects I remember to have seen in the heavens. The cluster appears under the form of a solid ball, consisting of small stars, quite compressed into one blaze of light, with a great number of loose ones surrounding it, and distinctly visible in the general mass. See fig. 2 [Plate I].

When I began my present series of observations, I surmised, that several nebulæ might yet remain undiscovered, for want of sufficient light to detect them; and was, therefore, in hopes of making a valuable addition to the clusters of stars and nebulæ already collected and given us in the work before referred to, which amount to 103. The event has plainly

[a] [M98=NGC 4192, a giant edge-on spiral in the Virgo cluster of galaxies.—D.]
[b] [M53=NGC 5024, a globular cluster well described by Herschel.—D.]

proved that my expectations were well founded: for I have already found 466 new nebulæ and clusters of stars, none of which, to my present knowledge, have been seen before by any person; most of them, indeed, are not within the reach of the best common telescopes now in use. In all probability many more are still in reserve; and as I am pursuing this track, I shall make them up into separate catalogues, of about two or three hundred at a time, and have the honour of presenting them in that form to the Royal Society.

A very remarkable circumstance attending the nebulæ and clusters of stars is, that they are arranged into strata, which seem to run on to a great length; and some of them I have already been able to pursue, so as to guess pretty well at their form and direction. It is probable enough, that they may surround the whole apparent sphere of the heavens, not unlike the milky way, which undoubtedly is nothing but a stratum of fixed stars. And as this latter immense starry bed is not of equal breadth or lustre in every part, nor runs on in one straight direction, but is curved and even divided into two streams along a very considerable portion of it; we may likewise expect the greatest variety in the strata of the clusters of stars and nebulæ. One of these nebulous beds is so rich, that, in passing through a section of it, in the time of only 36 minutes, I detected no less than 31 nebulæ, all distinctly visible upon a fine blue sky. Their situation and shape, as well as condition, seem to denote the greatest variety imaginable. In another stratum, or perhaps a different branch of the former, I have seen double and treble nebulæ, variously arranged; large ones with small, seeming attendants; narrow but much extended, lucid nebulæ or bright dashes; some of the shape of a fan, resembling an electric brush, issuing from a lucid point; others of the cometic shape, with a seeming nucleus in the center; or like cloudy stars, surrounded with a nebulous atmosphere; a different sort again contain a nebulosity of the milky kind, like that wonderful, inexplicable phænomenon about θ Orionis; while others shine with a fainter, mottled kind of light, which denotes their being resolvable into stars.[a] See fig. 3 [Plate I], &c. But it would be too extensive at present to enter more minutely into such circumstances, therefore I proceed with the subject of nebulous and sidereal strata.

It is very probable, that the great stratum, called the milky way, is that in which the sun is placed, though perhaps not in the very center of its thickness. We gather this from the appearance of the Galaxy, which seems

[a] [Herschel is here describing a wide variety of objects: both areas of sky in high galactic latitude containing many galaxies of different forms, and also ("that . . . inexplicable phænomenon about θ Orionis", i.e. the Orion nebula) galactic nebulæ.—D.]

to encompass the whole heavens, as it certainly must do if the sun is within the same. For, suppose a number of stars arranged between two parallel planes, indefinitely extended every way, but at a given considerable distance from each other; and, calling this a sidereal stratum, an eye placed somewhere within it will see all the stars in the direction of the planes of the stratum projected into a great circle, which will appear lucid on account of the accumulation of the stars; while the rest of the heavens, at the sides, will only seem to be scattered over with constellations, more or less crowded, according to the distance of the planes or number of stars contained in the thickness or sides of the stratum.

Thus, in [Plate 3] an eye at S within the stratum ab, will see the stars in the direction of its length ab, or height cd, with all those in the intermediate situations, projected into the lucid circle ACBD; while those in the sides mv, nw, will be seen scattered over the remaining part of the heavens at MVNW.

If the eye were placed somewhere without the stratum, at no very great distance, the appearance of the stars within it would assume the form of one of the less circles of the sphere, which would be more or less contracted to the distance of the eye; and if this distance were exceedingly increased, the whole stratum might at last be drawn together into a lucid spot of any shape, according to the position, length, and height of the stratum.

Let us now suppose, that a branch, or smaller stratum, should run out from the former, in a certain direction, and let it also be contained between two parallel planes extended indefinitely onwards, but so that the eye may be placed in the great stratum somewhere before the separation, and not far from the place where the strata are still united. Then will this second stratum not be projected into a bright circle like the former, but will be seen as a lucid branch proceeding from the first, and returning to it again at a certain distance less than a semi-circle.

Thus, in the same figure, the stars in the small stratum pq will be projected into a bright arch at PRRP, which, after its separation from the circle CBD, unites with it again at P.

What has been instanced in parallel planes may easily be applied to strata irregularly bounded, and running in various directions; for their projections will of consequence vary according to the quantities of the variations in the strata and the distance of the eye from the same. And thus any kind of curvatures, as well as various different degrees of brightness, may be produced in the projections.

From appearances then, as I observed before, we may infer, that the sun is most likely placed in one of the great strata of the fixed stars, and very probably not far from the place where some smaller stratum branches out from it. Such a supposition will satisfactorily, and with great simplicity, account for all the phænomena of the milky way, which, according to this hypothesis, is no other than the appearance of the projection of the stars contained in this stratum and its secondary branch. As a farther inducement to look on the Galaxy in this point of view, let it be considered, that we can no longer doubt of its whitish appearance arising from the mixed lustre of the numberless stars that compose it. Now, should we imagine it to be an irregular ring of stars, in the center nearly of which we must then suppose the sun to be placed, it will appear not a little extraordinary, that the sun, being a fixed star like those which compose this imagined ring, should just be in the center of such a multitude of celestial bodies, without any apparent reason for this singular distinction; whereas, on our supposition, every star in this stratum, not very near the termination of its length or height, will be so placed as also to have its own Galaxy, with only such variations in the form and lustre of it, as may arise from the particular situation of each star.

Various methods may be pursued to come to a full knowledge of the sun's place in the sidereal stratum, of which I shall only mention one as the most general and most proper for determining this important point, and which I have already begun to put in practice. I call it *Gaging the Heavens*, or the *Star-Gage*.[a] It consists in repeatedly taking the number of stars in ten fields of view of my reflector very near each other, and by adding their sums, and cutting off one decimal on the right, a mean of the contents of the heavens, in all the parts which are thus gaged, is obtained. By way of example, I have joined a short table, extracted from the gages contained in my journal, by which it appears, that the number of stars increases very fast as we approach the Via Lactea.

Thus, in the parallel from 92 to 94 degrees north polar distance, and R.A. 15 h. 10′, the star-gage runs up from 9·4 stars in the field to 18·6 in

| N.P.D. 92 to 94°. | | N.P.D. 78 to 80°. | |
|---|---|---|---|
| R.A. | Gage. | R.A. | Gage. |
| 15   10 | 9·4 | 11   16 | 3·1 |
| 15   22 | 10·6 | 12   31 | 3·4 |
| 15   47 | 10·6 | 12   44 | 4·6 |
| 16    8 | 12·1 | 12   49 | 3·9 |
| 16   25 | 13·6 | 13    5 | 3·8 |
| 16   37 | 18·6 | 14   30 | 3·6 |

[a] [A pioneering exercise in the collection and interpretation of stellar statistics.]

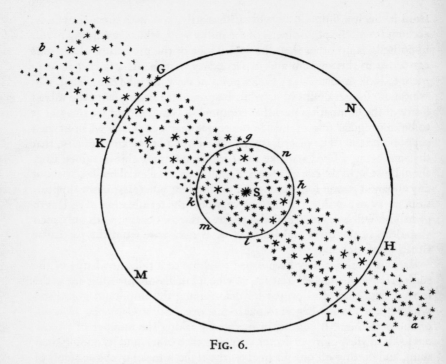

FIG. 6.

about an hour and a half; whereas in the parallel from 78° to 80° north polar distance, and R.A. 11, 12, 13, and 14 hours, it very seldom rises above 4. We are, however, to remember, that with different instruments the account of the gages will be very different, especially on our supposition of the situation of the sun in a stratum of stars. For, let *ab*, fig. 6, be the stratum, and suppose the small circle *ghlk* to represent the space into which, by the light and power of a given telescope, we may penetrate; and let GHLK be the extent of another portion, which we are enabled to visit by means of a larger aperture and power; it is evident, that the gages with the latter instrument will differ very much in their account of stars contained at MN, and at KG or LH; when with the former they will hardly be affected by the change from *mn* to *kg* or *lh*. And this accounts for what a celebrated author says concerning the effects of telescopes, by which we must understand the best of those that are in common use.[a]

[a] On voit avec les télescopes des étoiles dans toutes les parties du ciel, à peu près comme dans la voie lactée, ou dans les nébuleuses. On ne sauroit douter qu'une partie de l'éclat et de la blancheur de la voie lactée, ne provienne de la lumière des petites étoiles qui s'y trouvent en effet par millions; cependant, avec les plus

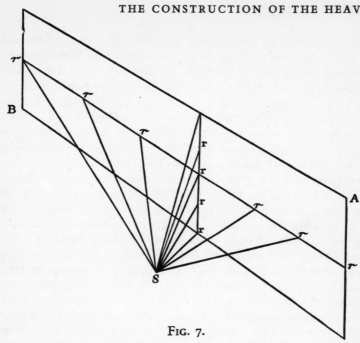

FIG. 7.

It would not be safe to enter into an application of these, and such other gages as I have already taken, till they are sufficiently continued and carried all over the heavens. I shall, therefore, content myself with just mentioning that the situation of the sun will be obtained, from considering in what manner the star-gage agrees with the length of a ray revolving in several directions about an assumed point, and cut off by the bounds of the stratum. Thus, in fig. 7, let S be the place of an observer; Srrr, Srrr, lines in the planes rSr, rSr, drawn from S within the stratum to one of the boundaries, here represented by the plane AB. Then, since neither the situation of S, nor the form of the limiting surface AB, is given, we are to assume a point, and apply to it lines proportional to the several gages that have been obtained, and at such angles from each other as they may point out; then will the termination of these lines delineate the boundary of the stratum, and consequently manifest the situation of the sun within the same. But to proceed.

grands télescopes, on n'en distingue pas assés, et elles n'y sont pas assés rapprochées les unes des autres pour qu'on puisse attribuer à celles qu'on distingue la blancheur de la voie lactée, si sensible à la vue simple. L'on ne sauroit donc prononcer que les étoiles soient la seule cause de cette blancheur, quoique nous ne connoissions aucune maniére satisfaisante de l'expliquer. *Ast.* M. DE LA LANDE, § 833.

If the sun should be placed in the great sidereal stratum of the milky way, and, as we have surmised above, not far from the branching out of a secondary stratum, it will very naturally lead us to guess at the cause of the probable motion of the solar system: for the very bright, great node of the Via Lactis, or union of the two strata about Cepheus and Cassiopeia, and the Scorpion and Sagittarius, points out a conflux of stars manifestly quite sufficient to occasion a tendency towards that node in any star situated at no very great distance; and the secondary branch of the Galaxy not being much less than a semi-circle seems to indicate such a situation of our solar system in the great undivided stratum as the most probable.

What has been said in a former paper [above, pp. 43–54] on the subject of the solar motion seems also to support this supposed situation of the sun; for the apex there assigned lies nearly in the direction of a motion of the sun towards the node of the strata. Besides, the joining stratum making a pretty large angle at the junction with the primary one, it may easily be admitted, that the motion of a star in the great stratum, especially if situated considerably towards the side farthest from the small stratum, will be turned sufficiently out of the straight direction of the great stratum towards the secondary one. But I find myself insensibly led to say more on this subject than I am as yet authorised to do; I will, therefore, return to those observations which have suggested the idea of celestial strata.

In my late observations on nebulæ I soon found, that I generally detected them in certain directions rather than in others; that the spaces preceding them were generally quite deprived of their stars, so as often to afford many fields without a single star in it; that the nebulæ generally appeared some time after among stars of a certain considerable size, and but seldom among very small stars; that when I came to one nebula, I generally found several more in the neighbourhood; that afterwards a considerable time passed before I came to another parcel; and these events being often repeated in different altitudes of my instrument, and some of them at a considerable distance from each other, it occurred to me, that the intermediate spaces between the sweeps might also contain nebulæ; and finding this to hold good more than once, I ventured to give notice to my assistant at the clock, "to prepare, since I expected in a few minutes to come at a stratum of the nebulæ, finding myself already" (as I then figuratively expressed it) "on nebulous ground." In this I succeeded immediately; so that I now can venture to point out several not far distant places, where I shall soon carry my telescope, in expectation of meeting with many nebulæ. But how far these circumstances of vacant places preceding and following the nebulous strata, and their being as it were contained in a bed of stars, sparingly scattered between them, may hold good in more distant portions of the heavens, and which I have not yet been able to visit in any regular manner, I ought by no means to hazard a conjecture. The subject is new, and we must attend to observations, and be guided by them, before we form general opinions.

Before I conclude, I may, however, venture to add a few particulars about the direction of some of the capital strata or their branches. The well known nebula of Cancer,[a] visible to the naked eye, is probably one belonging to a certain stratum, in which I suppose it to be so placed as to lie nearest to us. This stratum I shall call that of Cancer. It runs from ε Cancri towards the south over the 67 nebula of the *Connoissance des Temps*, which is a very beautiful and pretty much compressed cluster of stars, easily to be seen by any good telescope, and in which I have observed above 200 stars at once in the field of view of my great reflector, with a power of 157. This cluster appearing so plainly with any good, common telescope, and being so near to the one which may be seen by the naked eye, denotes it to be probably the next in distance to that within the quartile formed by $\gamma$, $\delta$, $\eta$, $\theta$; from the 67th nebula the stratum of Cancer proceeds towards the head of Hydra; but I have not yet had time to trace it farther than the equator.

Another stratum, which perhaps approaches nearer to the solar system than any of the rest, and whose situation is nearly at rectangles to the great sidereal stratum in which the sun is placed, is that of Coma Berenices,[b] as

[a] ["well known nebula of Cancer"=M44, Praesepe, a near-by galactic star cluster resolvable with the slightest optical aid, as Herschel well knew. What Herschel had in mind as the "stratum of Cancer" is not very clear: probably the association of M44 and M67 (another galactic cluster) with the numerous faint naked-eye stars that make up the constellation of Cancer, stretching down to Hydra. With M44 they give this part of the sky a hazy appearance at a first glance. There is no unusually great number of galaxies here.—D.]

[b] [The stratum of Coma Berenices is very different. Described, for the greater part correctly by Herschel, it is an elongated area of sky running up through Virgo and Coma into Ursa Major (though not beyond), remarkably rich in galaxies. It contains the Virgo cluster of galaxies and has recently been called the 'supergalaxy': Herschel was the first to recognize it. (See Plate 2) "the Coma itself", i.e. the loose cluster of stars that form the constellation of Coma Berenices, is of course a fortuitous foreground object.

(Note the confusion of thought here: Herschel has not clearly distinguished in his mind between strata of stars (the Galaxy), star clusters, and galaxies. In modern terms the stratum of Coma Berenices is an elongated association of galaxies. Herschel thought of it as being a stratum of stars mostly grouped in clusters, of which only Coma Berenices was near enough to be resolved. He probably had a similar picture of the "stratum of Cancer".)—D.]

I shall call it. I suppose the Coma itself to be one of the clusters in it, and that, on account of its nearness, it appears to be so scattered. It has many capital nebulæ very near it; and in all probability this stratum runs on a very considerable way. It may, perhaps, even make the circuit of the heavens, though very likely not in one of the great circles of the sphere: for, unless it should chance to intersect the great sidereal stratum of the milky way before-mentioned, in the very place in which the sun is stationed, such an appearance could hardly be produced. However, if the stratum of Coma Berenices should extend so far as (by taking in the assistance of M. MESSIER's and M. MECHAIN's excellent observations of scattered nebulæ, and some detached former observations of my own) I apprehend it may, the direction of it towards the north lies probably, with some windings, through the great Bear onwards to Cassiopeia; thence through the girdle of Andromeda and the northern Fish, proceeding towards Cetus; while towards the south it passes through the Virgin, probably on to the tail of Hydra and the head of Centaurus. But, notwithstanding I have already fully ascertained the existence and direction of this stratum for more than 30 degrees of a great circle, and found it almost every where equally rich in fine nebulæ, it still might be dangerous to proceed in more extensive conjectures, that have as yet no more than a precarious foundation. I shall therefore wait till the observations in which I am at present engaged shall furnish me with proper materials for the disquisition of so new a subject. And though my single endeavours should not succeed in a work that seems to require the joint effort of every astronomer, yet so much we may venture to hope, that, by applying ourselves with all our powers to the improvement of telescopes, which I look upon as yet in their infant state, and turning them with assiduity to the study of the heavens, we shall in time obtain some faint knowledge of, and perhaps be able partly to delineate, *the Interior Construction of the Universe*.

Datchet near Windsor,                    WILLIAM HERSCHEL.
    April, 1784.

# On the Construction of the Heavens.[a]

Read February 3, 1785.

THE subject of the Construction of the Heavens, on which I have so lately ventured to deliver my thoughts to this Society, is of so extensive and important a nature, that we cannot exert too much attention in our endeavours to throw all possible light upon it; I shall, therefore, now

[a] [*Phil. Trans.*, LXXV (1785), 213–66.]

attempt to pursue the delineations of which a faint outline was begun in my former paper.

By continuing to observe the heavens with my last constructed, and since that time much improved instrument, I am now enabled to bring more confirmation to several parts that were before but weakly supported, and also to offer a few still further extended hints, such as they present themselves to my present view. But first let me mention that, if we would hope to make any progress in an investigation of this delicate nature, we ought to avoid two opposite extremes, of which I can hardly say which is the most dangerous. If we indulge a fanciful imagination and build worlds of our own, we must not wonder at our going wide from the path of truth and nature; but these will vanish like the Cartesian vortices, that soon gave way when better theories were offered. On the other hand, if we add observation to observation, without attempting to draw not only certain conclusions, but also conjectural views from them, we offend against the very end for which only observations ought to be made. I will endeavour to keep a proper medium; but if I should deviate from that, I could wish not to fall into the latter error.

That the milky way is a most extensive stratum of stars of various sizes admits no longer of the least doubt; and that our sun is actually one of the heavenly bodies belonging to it is as evident. I have now viewed and gaged this shining zone in almost every direction, and find it composed of stars whose number, by the account of these gages, constantly increases and decreases in proportion to its apparent brightness to the naked eye. But in order to develop the ideas of the universe, that have been suggested by my late observations, it will be best to take the subject from a point of view at a considerable distance both of space and of time.

### Theoretical view.

Let us then suppose numberless stars of various sizes, scattered over an indefinite portion of space in such a manner as to be almost equally distributed throughout the whole. The laws of attraction, which no doubt extend to the remotest regions of the fixed stars, will operate in such a manner as most probably to produce the following remarkable effects.

### Formation of nebulæ.

Form I.[a] In the first place, since we have supposed the stars to be of

[a] [These four *Forms* of nebulæ, referred to by Herschel in papers about this time, are not to be confused with the eight *Classes* of nebulæ and clusters into which Herschel divided his objects on observational grounds, and which classify objects in his catalogues. For these classes see note on p. 119.—D.]

various sizes, it will frequently happen that a star, being considerably larger than its neighbouring ones, will attract them more than they will be attracted by others that are immediately around them; by which means they will be, in time, as it were, condensed about a center; or, in other words, form themselves into a cluster of stars of almost a globular figure, more or less regularly so, according to the size and original distance of the surrounding stars. The perturbations of these mutual attractions must undoubtedly be very intricate, as we may easily comprehend by considering what Sir ISAAC NEWTON says in the first book of his *Principia*, in the 38th and following problems; but in order to apply this great author's reasoning of bodies moving in ellipses to such as are here, for a while, supposed to have no other motion than what their mutual gravity has imparted to them, we must suppose the conjugate axes of these ellipses indefinitely diminished, whereby the ellipses will become straight lines.

Form II. The next case, which will also happen almost as frequently as the former, is where a few stars, though not superior in size to the rest, may chance to be rather nearer each other than the surrounding ones; for here also will be formed a prevailing attraction in the combined center of gravity of them all, which will occasion the neighbouring stars to draw together; not indeed so as to form a regular or globular figure, but however in such a manner as to be condensed towards the common center of gravity of the whole irregular cluster. And this construction admits of the utmost variety of shapes, according to the number and situation of the stars which first gave rise to the condensation of the rest.

Form III. From the composition and repeated conjunction of both the foregoing forms, a third may be derived, when many large stars, or combined small ones, are situated in long extended, regular, or crooked rows, hooks, or branches; for they will also draw the surrounding ones, so as to produce figures of condensed stars coarsely similar to the former which gave rise to these condensations.

Form IV. We may likewise admit of still more extensive combinations; when, at the same time that a cluster of stars is forming in one part of space, there may be another collecting in a different, but perhaps not far distant quarter, which may occasion a mutual approach towards their common center of gravity.

V. In the last place, as a natural consequence of the former cases, there will be formed great cavities or vacancies by the retreat of the stars towards the various centers which attract them; so that upon the whole there is evidently a field of the greatest variety for the mutual and combined attractions of the heavenly bodies to exert themselves in. I shall, therefore, without extending myself farther upon this subject, proceed to a few considerations, that will naturally occur to every one who may view this subject in the light I have here done.

## Objections considered.

At first sight then it will seem as if a system, such as it has been displayed in the foregoing paragraphs, would evidently tend to a general destruction, by the shock of one star's falling upon another. It would here be a sufficient answer to say, that if observation should prove this really to be the system of the universe, there is no doubt but that the great Author of it has amply provided for the preservation of the whole, though it should not appear to us in what manner this is effected. But I shall moreover point out several circumstances that do manifestly tend to a general preservation; as, in the first place, the indefinite extent of the sidereal heavens, which must produce a balance that will effectually secure all the great parts of the whole from approaching to each other. There remains then only to see how the particular stars belonging to separate clusters will be preserved from rushing on to their centers of attraction. And here I must observe, that though I have before, by way of rendering the case more simple, considered the stars as being originally at rest, I intended not to exclude projectile forces; and the admission of them will prove such a barrier against the seeming destructive power of attraction as to secure from it all the stars belonging to a cluster, if not for ever, at least for millions of ages. Besides, we ought perhaps to look upon such clusters, and the destruction of now and then a star, in some thousands of ages, as perhaps the very means by which the whole is preserved and renewed. These clusters may be the *Laboratories* of the universe, if I may so express myself, wherein the most salutary remedies for the decay of the whole are prepared.

## Optical appearances.

From this theoretical view of the heavens, which has been taken, as we observed, from a point not less distant in time than in space, we will now retreat to our own retired station, in one of the planets attending a star in its great combination with numberless others;[a] and in order to investigate what will be the appearances from this contracted situation, let us begin with the naked eye. The stars of the first magnitude being in all probability the nearest, will furnish us with a step to begin our scale; setting off, therefore, with the distance of Sirius or Arcturus, for instance, as unity, we will at present suppose, that those of the second magnitude are at double,

[a] [In Herschel's manuscript, heavily deleted but just legible, are the words: "that make up a cluster, which itself is but one of the minute parts of an indefinite whole".]

and those of the third at treble the distance, and so forth. It is not necessary critically to examine what quantity of light or magnitude of a star intitles it to be estimated of such or such a proportional distance, as the common coarse estimation will answer our present purpose as well; taking it then for granted, that a star of the seventh magnitude is about seven times as far as one of the first, it follows, that an observer, who is inclosed in a globular cluster of stars, and not far from the center, will never be able, with the naked eye, to see to the end of it: for, since, according to the above estimations, he can only extend his view to about seven times the distance of Sirius, it cannot be expected that his eyes should reach the borders of a cluster which has perhaps not less than fifty stars in depth every where around him. The whole universe, therefore, to him will be comprised in a set of constellations, richly ornamented with scattered stars of all sizes. Or if the united brightness of a neighbouring cluster of stars should, in a remarkable clear night, reach his sight, it will put on the appearance of a small, faint, whitish, nebulous cloud, not to be perceived without the greatest attention. To pass by other situations, let him be placed in a much extended stratum, or branching cluster of millions of stars, such as may fall under the IIIa form of nebulæ considered in a fore-going paragraph. Here also the heavens will not only be richly scattered over with brilliant constellations, but a shining zone or milky way will be perceived to surround the whole sphere of the heavens, owing to the combined light of those stars which are too small, that is, too remote to be seen. Our observer's sight will be so confined, that he will imagine this single collection of stars, of which he does not even perceive the thousandth part, to be the whole contents of the heavens. Allowing him now the use of a common telescope, he begins to suspect that all the milkiness of the bright path which surrounds the sphere may be owing to stars. He perceives a few clusters of them in various parts of the heavens, and finds also that there are a kind of nebulous patches; but still his views are not extended so far as to reach to the end of the stratum in which he is situated, so that he looks upon these patches as belonging to that system which to him seems to comprehend every celestial object. He now increases his power of vision, and, applying himself to a close observation, finds that the milky way is indeed no other than a collection of very small stars. He perceives that those objects which had been called nebulæ are evidently nothing but clusters of stars. He finds their number increase upon him, and when he resolves one nebula into stars he discovers ten new ones which he cannot resolve. He then forms the idea of immense strata of fixed stars, of clusters of stars and of nebulæ;[a] till, going on with such

[a] See a former paper on the Construction of the Heavens.

interesting observations, he now perceives that all these appearances must naturally arise from the confined situation in which we are placed. *Confined* it may justly be called, though in no less a space than what before appeared to be the whole region of the fixed stars; but which now has assumed the shape of a crookedly branching nebula; not, indeed, one of the least, but perhaps very far from being the most considerable of those numberless clusters that enter into the construction of the heavens.

### Result of Observations.

I shall now endeavour to shew, that the theoretical view of the system of the universe, which has been exposed in the foregoing part of this paper, is perfectly consistent with facts, and seems to be confirmed and established by a series of observations. It will appear, that many hundreds of nebulæ of the first and second forms are actually to be seen in the heavens, and their places will hereafter be pointed out. Many of the third form will be described, and instances of the fourth related. A few of the cavities mentioned in the fifth will be particularised, though many more have already been observed; so that, upon the whole, I believe, it will be found, that the foregoing theoretical view, with all its consequential appearances, as seen by an eye inclosed in one of the nebulæ, is no other than a drawing from nature, wherein the features of the original have been closely copied; and I hope the resemblance will not be called a bad one, when it shall be considered how very limited must be the pencil of an inhabitant of so small and retired a portion of an indefinite system in attempting the picture of so unbounded an extent.

But to proceed to particulars: I shall begin by giving the following table of gages that have been taken. In the first column is the right ascension, and in the second the north polar distance, both reduced to the time of FLAMSTEED's Catalogue. In the third are the contents of the heavens, being the result of the gages. The fourth shews from how many fields of view the gages were deduced, which have been ten or more where the number of the stars was not very considerable; but, as it would have taken too much time, in high numbers, to count so many fields, the gages are generally single. Where the stars happened to be uncommonly crowded, no more than half a field was counted, and even sometimes only a quadrant; but then it was always done with the precaution of fixing on some row of stars that would point out the division of the field, so as to prevent any considerable mistake. When five, ten, or more fields are gaged, the polar distance in the second column of the table is that of the middle of the sweep, which was generally from 2 to $2\frac{1}{2}$ degrees in breadth;

and, in gaging, a regular distribution of the fields, from the bottom of the sweep to the top, was always strictly attended to. The fifth column contains occasional remarks relating to the gages.

I. Table of Star-Gages.

| R.A. | | | P.D. | | Stars. | Fields. | Memorandum |
|---|---|---|---|---|---|---|---|
| 0$^h$ | 1′ | 41″ | 78$^d$ | 47′ | 9·9 | 10 | |
| 0 | 4 | 55 | 65 | 36 | 20·0 | 10 | |
| 0 | 7 | 54 | 74 | 13 | 11·3 | 10 | Most of the stars extremely |
| 0 | 8 | 24 | 49 | 7 | 60 | 1 | small. |
| 0 | 9 | 52 | 113 | 17 | 4·1 | 10 | * |
| | | | | | | | |
| 23 | 46 | 55 | 65 | 36 | 15·3 | 10 | |
| 23 | 59 | 21 | 87 | 10 | 5·6 | 10 | |
| 23 | 59 | 56 | 95 | 4 | 7·8 | 10 | |

[135 sets of five gages each are not reproduced.]

## PROBLEM.

*The stars being supposed to be nearly equally scattered, and their number, in a field of view of a known angular diameter, being given, to determine the length of the visual ray.*

Here, the arrangement of the stars not being fixed upon, we must endeavour to find which way they may be placed so as to fill a given space most equally. Suppose a rectangular cone cut into frustula by many equi-distant planes perpendicular to the axis; then, if one star be placed at the vertex, and another in the axis at the first intersection, six stars may be set around it so as to be equally distant from one another and from the central star. These positions being carried on in the same manner, we shall have every star within the cone surrounded by eight others, at an equal distance from that star taken as a center. [Plate 4, left] contains four sections of such a cone distinguished by alternate shades, which will be sufficient to explain what sort of arrangement I would point out.

The series of the number of stars contained in the several sections will be 1 . 7 . 19 . 37 . 61 . 91 . &c. which continued to $n$ terms, the sum of it, by the differential method, will be $na + n \cdot \frac{n-1}{2}d' + n \cdot \frac{n-1}{2} \cdot \frac{n-2}{2}d''$,

* The gages marked with an asterisk are those by which Fig. 8 [page 96] has been delineated.

&c.: where $a$ is the first term, $d'$, $d''$, $d'''$, &c. the 1st, 2d, and 3d differences. Then, since $a=1$, $d'=6$, $d''=6$, $d'''=0$, the sum of the series will be $n^3$. Let S be the given number of stars; 1, the diameter of the base of the field of view; and B, the diameter of the base of the great rectangular cone; and, by trigonometry, we shall have $B=\dfrac{\text{Radius}}{\text{Tang. } \frac{1}{2} \text{ field}}$. Now, since the field of view of a telescope is a cone, we shall have its solidity to that of the great cone of stars, formed by the above construction, as the square of the diameter of the base of the field of view, to the square of the diameter of the base of the great cone, the height of both being the same; and the stars in each cone being in the ratio of the solidity, as being equally scattered,[a] we have $n=\sqrt[3]{B^2S}$. And the length of the visual ray $=n-1$, which was to be determined. . . .

[A variant of this calculation is not reproduced.]

### We inhabit the planet of a star belonging to a Compound Nebula of the third form.

I shall now proceed to shew that the stupendous sidereal system we inhabit, this extensive stratum and its secondary branch, consisting of many millions of stars, is, in all probability, *a detached Nebula*. In order to

[a] We ought to remark, that the periphery and base of the cone of the field of view, in gaging, would in all probability seldom fall exactly on such stars as would produce a perfect equality of situation between the stars contained in the small and the great cone; and that, consequently, the solution of this problem, where we suppose the stars of one cone to be to those of the other in the ratio of the solidity on account of their being equally scattered, will not be strictly true. But it should be remembered, that in small numbers, where the different terminations of the fields would most affect this solution, the stars in view have always been ascertained from gages that were often repeated, and each of which consisted of no less than ten fields successively taken, so that the different deviations at the periphery and base of the cone would certainly compensate each other sufficiently for the purpose of this calculation. And that, on the other hand, in high gages, which could not have the advantage of being so often repeated, these deviations would bear a much smaller proportion to the great number of stars in a field of view; and therefore, on this account, such gages may very justly be admitted in a solution where practical truth rather than mathematical precision is the end we have in view. It is moreover not to be supposed that we imagine the stars to be actually arranged in this regular manner, and, returning therefore to our general hypothesis of their being equally scattered, any one field of view promiscuously taken may, in this general sense, be supposed to contain a due proportion of them; so that the principle on which this solution is founded may therefore be said to be even more rigorously true than we have occasion to insist upon in an argument of this kind.

go upon grounds that seem to me to be capable of great certainty, they being no less than an actual survey of the boundaries of our sidereal system, which I have plainly perceived, as far as I have yet gone round it, every where terminated, and in most places very narrowly too, it will be proper to shew the length of my sounding line, if I may so call it, that it may appear whether it was sufficiently long for the purpose.

In the most crowded part of the milky way I have had fields of view that contained no less than 588 stars,[a] and these were continued for many minutes, so that in one quarter of an hour's time there passed no less than 116000 stars through the field of view of my telescope.[b] Now, if we compute the length of the visual ray by putting $S = 588$, and the diameter of the field of view fifteen minutes, we shall find $n = \sqrt[3]{B^2S} = 498$; so that it appears the length of what I have called my sounding line, or $n-1$, was probably not less than 497 times the distance of Sirius from the sun. . . .

It may seem inaccurate that we should found an argument on the stars being equally scattered, when in all probability there may not be two of them in the heavens, whose mutual distance shall be equal to that of any other two given stars; but it should be considered, that when we take all the stars collectively there will be a mean distance which may be assumed as the general one; and an argument founded on such a supposition will have in its favour the greatest probability of not being far short of truth. What will render the supposition of an equal distribution of the stars, with regard to the gages, still less exposed to objections is, that whenever the stars happened either to be uncommonly crowded or deficient in number, so as very suddenly to pass over from one extreme to the other, the gages were reduced to other forms, such as the border-gage, the distance-gage, &c. which terms, and the use of such gages, I shall hereafter find an opportunity of explaining. And none of those kinds of gages have been admitted in this table, which consists only of such as have been taken in places where the stars apparently seemed to be, in general, pretty evenly scattered; and to increase and decrease in number by a certain gradual progression. Nor has any part of the heavens containing a cluster of stars been put in the gages; and here I must observe, that the difference between

[a] See the table of Gages.

[b] The breadth of my sweep was 2° 26', to which must be added 15' for two semi-diameters of the field. Then putting $161 = a$, the number of fields in 15 minutes of time; $\cdot 7854 = b$, the proportion of a circle to 1, its circumscribed square; $\phi = $ sine of 74° 22', the polar distance of the middle of the sweep reduced to the present time; and $588 = S$, the number of stars in a field of view, we have $\frac{a\phi S}{b} = 116076$ stars.

a crowded place and a cluster may easily be perceived by the arrangement as well as the size and mutual distance of the stars: for in a cluster they are generally not only resembling each other pretty nearly in size, but a certain uniformity of distance also takes place; they are more and more accumulated towards the center, and put on all the appearances which we should naturally expect from a number of them collected into a group at a certain distance from us. On the other hand, the rich parts of the milky way, as well as those in the distant broad part of the stratum, consist of a mixture of stars of all possible sizes, that are seemingly placed without any particular apparent order. Perhaps we might recollect, that a greater condensation towards the center of our system than towards the borders of it should be taken into consideration; but, with a nebula of the third form, containing such various and extensive combinations, as I have found to take place in ours, this circumstance, which in one of the first form would be of considerable moment, may, I think, be safely neglected. However, I would not be understood to lay a greater stress on these and the following calculations than the principles on which they are founded will permit; and if hereafter we shall find reason, from experience and observation, to believe that there are parts of our system where the stars are not scattered in the manner here supposed, we ought then to make proper exceptions.

But to return: if some other high gage be selected from the table, such as 472 or 344, the length of the visual ray will be found 461 and 415. And although, in consequence of what has been said, a certain degree of doubt may be left about the arrangement and scattering of the stars, yet when I recollect, that in those parts of the milky way where these high gages were taken, the stars were neither so small, nor so crowded, as they must have been on a supposition of a much farther continuance of them, when certainly a milky or nebulous appearance must have come on, I need not fear to have over-rated the extent of my visual ray. And indeed every thing that can be said to shorten it will only contract the limits of our nebula, as it has in most places been of sufficient length to go far beyond the bounds of it. Thus, in the sides of the stratum opposite to our situation in it, where the gages often run below 5, our nebula cannot extend to 100 times the distance of Sirius; and the same telescope, which could shew 588 stars in a field of view of 15 minutes, must certainly have presented me also with the stars in these situations as well as the former, had they been there. If we should answer this by observing that they might be at too great a distance to be perceived, it will be allowing that there must at least be a vacancy amounting to the length of a visual ray not short of 400 times the distance of Sirius; and this is amply sufficient to make our nebula a detached one. It is true, that it would not be consistent confidently to affirm that we were on an island unless we had actually found ourselves every where bounded by the ocean, and therefore I shall go no farther than the gages will authorise; but considering the little depth of the stratum in all those places which have been actually gaged, to which must be added all the intermediate parts that have been viewed and found to be much like the rest, there is but little room to expect a connection between our nebula and any of the neighbouring ones. I ought also to add, that a telescope with a much larger aperture than my present one, grasping together a greater quantity of light, and thereby enabling us to see farther into space, will be the surest means of compleating and establishing the arguments that have been used: for if our nebula is not absolutely a detached one, I am firmly persuaded, that an instrument may be made large enough to discover the places where the stars continue onwards. A very bright milky nebulosity must there undoubtedly come on, since the stars in a field of view will increase in the ratio of $n^3$, greater than that of the cube of the visual ray. Thus, if 588 stars in a given field of view are to be seen by a ray of 497 times the distance of Sirius; when this is lengthened to 1000, which is but little more than double the former, the number of stars in the same field of view will be no less than 4774: for when the visual ray $r$ is given, the number S of stars will be $= \dfrac{n^3}{B^2}$; where

$n=r+1$; and a telescope with a three-fold power of extending into space, or with a ray of 1500, which, I think, may easily be constructed, will give us 16096 stars. Now, these would not be so close but that a good power applied to such an instrument might easily distinguish them; for they need not, if arranged in regular squares, approach nearer to each other than 6″·27; but what would produce the milky nebulosity which I have mentioned is the numberless stars beyond them, which in one respect the visual ray might also be said to reach. To make this appear we must return to the naked eye, which, as we have before estimated, can only see the stars of the seventh magnitude so as to distinguish them; but it is nevertheless very evident that the united lustre of millions of stars, such as I suppose the nebula in Andromeda to be, will reach our sight in the shape of a very small, faint nebulosity; since the nebula of which I speak may easily be seen in a fine evening. In the same manner my present telescope, as I have argued, has not only a visual ray that will reach the stars at 497 times the distance of Sirius so as to distinguish them (and probably much farther), but also a power of shewing the united lustre of the accumulated stars that compose a milky nebulosity, at a distance far exceeding the former limits; so that from these considerations it appears again highly

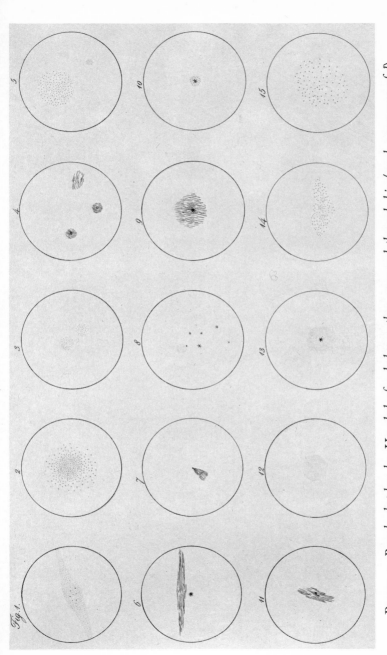

PLATE 1. *Rough sketches by Herschel of nebulae as they appeared through his (much more powerful) telescope, illustrating his 1784 paper on the construction of the heavens (see pp. 74–5).*

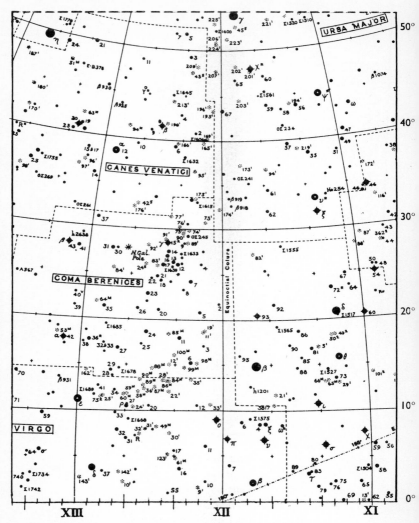

PLATE 2. *"The stratum of Coma Berenices"* (*see pp. 81–2, especially p. 81, note b*). *Chart of the sky near the North Galactic Pole, with stars indicated by circles and nebulæ by clusters of dots. Nebulæ numbers with superfix 'M' are from Messier's list; those with numeral superfix are from the corresponding class in Herschel's catalogues.* (*From Norton's Star Atlas, by courtesy of Messrs. Gall and Inglis.*)

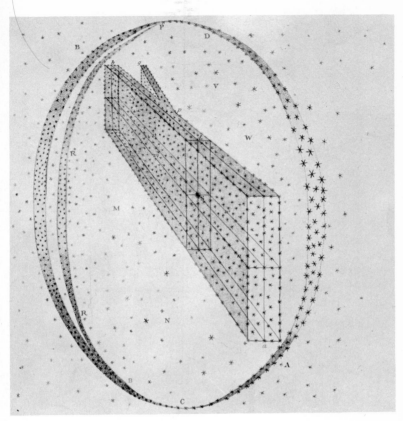

PLATE 3. *Herschel's explanation of the Milky Way. The Sun is embedded at S in a stratum of stars; to an observer near the Sun the stratum appears as a luminous band around the sky. The substance of this was first suggested by Thomas Wright in 1750 (see pp. 115–16). (Illustration to Herschel's 1784 paper on the construction of the heavens, see p. 76.)*

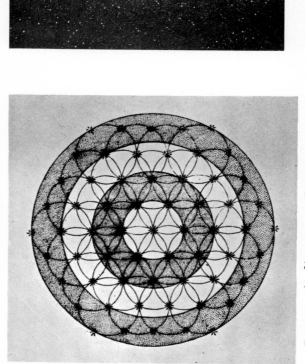

PLATE 4. (Left) *Diagram illustrating Herschel's calculation of the length of a visual ray in space in which stars are distributed uniformly (from his 1785 paper on the construction of the heavens, see p. 88). (Right) The globular cluster, M3, described by Herschel as one of "the most magnificently constructed sidereal systems" (p. 160). For his analysis of globular clusters, see pp. 107–15.*

PLATE 5. *"A most singular phænomenon!" The planetary nebula NGC 1514, observed by Herschel on 13 November 1790. He had previously supposed that if he could not detect individual stars in a patch of light this was because his instruments were not powerful enough. But this (gaseous) shell was so obviously associated with the central star that he reversed his opinion and admitted the existence of "true nebulosity"* (see pp. 118–29).

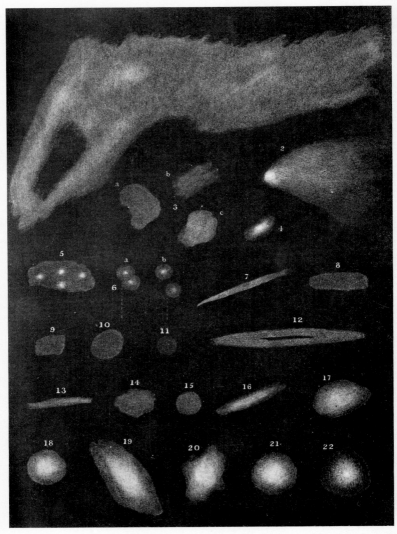

PLATE 6. *Rough sketches by Herschel of 'nebulosities' and 'nebulæ', illustrating his 1811 paper on the construction of the heavens* (pp. 136–44).

PLATE 7. *Rough sketches by Herschel of 'nebulæ', illustrating his 1811 paper on the construction of the heavens* (pp. 144–6).

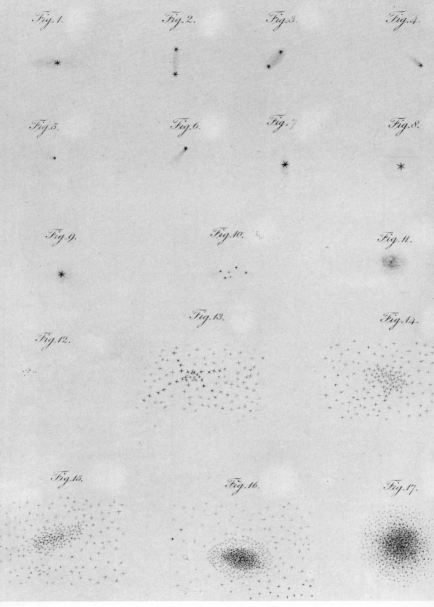

PLATE 8. *Rough sketches by Herschel to illustrate his 1814 paper on the connection of the sidereal part of the heavens to the nebulous part* (see pp. 151–60).

probable, that my present telescope, not shewing such a nebulosity in the milky way, goes already far beyond its extent: and consequently, much more would an instrument, such as I have mentioned, remove all doubt on the subject, both by shewing the stars in the continuation of the stratum, and by exposing a very strong milky nebulosity beyond them, that could no longer be mistaken for the dark ground of the heavens.

To these arguments, which rest on the firm basis of a series of observations, we may add the following considerations drawn from analogy. Among the great number of nebulæ which I have now already seen, amounting to more than 900, there are many which in all probability are equally extensive with that which we inhabit; and yet they are all separated from each other by very considerable intervals. Some indeed there are that seem to be double and treble; and though with most of these it may be, that they are at a very great distance from each other, yet we allow that some such conjunctions really are to be found; nor is this what we mean to exclude. But then these compound or double nebulæ, which are those of the third and fourth forms, still make a detached link in the great chain. It is also to be supposed, that there may still be some thinly scattered solitary stars between the large interstices of nebulæ, which, being situated so as to be nearly equally attracted by the several clusters when they were forming, remain unassociated. And though we cannot expect to see these stars, on account of their vast distance, yet we may well presume, that their number cannot be very considerable in comparison to those that are already drawn into systems; which conjecture is also abundantly confirmed in situations where the nebulæ are near enough to have their stars visible; for they are all insulated, and generally to be seen upon a very clear and pure ground, without any star near them that might be supposed to belong to them. And though I have often seen them in beds of stars, yet from the size of these latter we may be certain, that they were much nearer to us than those nebulæ, and belonged undoubtedly to our own system.

### Use of the gages.

A delineation of our nebula, by an application of the gages in the manner which·has been proposed to be done in my former paper, may now be attempted, and the following table is calculated for this purpose. It gives us the length of the visual ray for any number of stars in the field of view contained in the third column of the foregoing table of gages from $\frac{1}{10}$ to 100000. If the number required is not to be found in the first column of this table, a proportional mean may be taken between the two nearest rays in the second column, without any material error, except in

## TABLE II.

| Stars in the field. | Visual ray. | Stars. | Ray. | Stars. | Ray. | Stars. | Ray. | Stars. | Ray. |
|---|---|---|---|---|---|---|---|---|---|
|  |  | 31 | 186 | 71 | 245 | 210 | 352 | 700 | 527 |
| 0·1 | 27 | 32 | 188 | 72 | 246 | 220 | 358 | 800 | 551 |
| 0·2 | 34 | 33 | 190 | 73 | 247 | 230 | 363 | 900 | 573 |
| 0·3 | 39 | 34 | 192 | 74 | 249 | 240 | 368 | 1000 | 593 |
| 0·4 | 43 | 35 | 193 | 75 | 250 | 250 | 374 | 10000 | 1280 |
| 0·5 | 46 | 36 | 195 | 76 | 251 | 260 | 378 | 100000 | 2758 |
| 0·6 | 49 | 37 | 197 | 77 | 252 | 270 | 383 |  |  |
| 0·7 | 52 | 38 | 199 | 78 | 253 | 280 | 388 |  |  |
| 0·8 | 54 | 39 | 201 | 79 | 254 | 290 | 393 |  |  |
| 0·9 | 56 | 40 | 202 | 80 | 255 | 300 | 397 |  |  |
| 1 | 58 | 41 | 204 | 81 | 256 | 310 | 401 |  |  |
| 2 | 74 | 42 | 206 | 82 | 257 | 320 | 406 | 636175 | |
| 3 | 85 | 43 | 207 | 83 | 258 | 330 | 410 | or | |
| 4 | 93 | 44 | 209 | 84 | 259 | 340 | 414 | resolvable | 5112 |
| 5 | 101 | 45 | 210 | 85 | 260 | 350 | 418 | nebulosity | |
| 6 | 107 | 46 | 212 | 86 | 261 | 360 | 422 |  |  |
| 7 | 113 | 47 | 214 | 87 | 262 | 370 | 426 |  |  |
| 8 | 118 | 48 | 215 | 88 | 263 | 380 | 430 |  |  |
| 9 | 123 | 49 | 217 | 89 | 264 | 390 | 433 |  |  |
| 10 | 127 | 50 | 218 | 90 | 265 | 400 | 437 |  |  |
| 11 | 131 | 51 | 219 | 91 | 266 | 410 | 441 |  |  |
| 12 | 135 | 52 | 221 | 92 | 267 | 420 | 444 | 2544700 | |
| 13 | 139 | 53 | 222 | 93 | 268 | 430 | 448 | or | |
| 14 | 142 | 54 | 224 | 94 | 269 | 440 | 451 | milky | 8115 |
| 15 | 146 | 55 | 225 | 95 | 270 | 450 | 455 | nebulosity | |
| 16 | 149 | 56 | 226 | 96 | 271 | 460 | 458 |  |  |
| 17 | 152 | 57 | 228 | 97 | 272 | 470 | 461 |  |  |
| 18 | 155 | 58 | 229 | 98 | 273 | 480 | 464 |  |  |
| 19 | 158 | 59 | 230 | 99 | 274 | 490 | 468 |  |  |
| 20 | 160 | 60 | 232 | 100 | 275 | 500 | 471 |  |  |
| 21 | 163 | 61 | 233 | 110 | 284 | 510 | 474 |  |  |
| 22 | 166 | 62 | 234 | 120 | 291 | 520 | 477 |  |  |
| 23 | 168 | 63 | 236 | 130 | 300 | 530 | 480 |  |  |
| 24 | 170 | 64 | 237 | 140 | 308 | 540 | 483 |  |  |
| 25 | 173 | 65 | 238 | 150 | 315 | 550 | 486 |  |  |
| 26 | 175 | 66 | 239 | 160 | 322 | 560 | 489 |  |  |
| 27 | 177 | 67 | 240 | 170 | 328 | 570 | 492 |  |  |
| 28 | 180 | 68 | 242 | 180 | 335 | 580 | 495 |  |  |
| 29 | 182 | 69 | 243 | 190 | 341 | 590 | 498 |  |  |
| 30 | 184 | 70 | 244 | 200 | 347 | 600 | 500 |  |  |

the few last numbers. The calculations of resolvable and milky nebulosity, at the end of the table, are founded, the first, on a supposition of the stars being so crowded as to have only a square second of space allowed them; the next assigning them only half a second square. However, we should consider that in all probability a very different accumulation of stars may take place in different nebulæ; by which means some of them may assume the milky appearance, though not near so far removed from us; while clusters of stars also may become resolvable nebulæ from the same cause. The distinctness of the instrument is here also concerned; and as telescopes with large apertures are not easily brought to a good figure, nebulous appearances of both sorts may probably come on much before the distance annexed to them in the table.

### Section 0, our sidereal system.

By taking out of this table the visual rays which answer to the gages, and applying lines proportional to them around a point, according to their respective right ascensions and north polar distances, we may delineate a solid by means of the ends of these lines, which will give us so many points in its surface; I shall, however, content myself at present with a section only. I have taken one which passes through the poles of our system, and is at rectangles to the conjunction of the branches which I have called its length. The name of poles seemed to me not improperly applied to those points which are 90 degrees distant from a circle passing along the milky way, and the north pole is here assumed to be situated in R.A. 186° and P.D. 58°. The section represented in fig. 8 is one which makes an angle of 35 degrees with our equator, crossing it in 124½ and 304½ degrees. A celestial globe, adjusted to the latitude of 55° north, and having σ Ceti near the meridian, will have the plane of this section pointed out by the horizon, and the gages which have been used in this delineation are those which in table I. are marked by asterisks. When the visual rays answering to them are taken out of the second table, they must be projected on the plane of the horizon of the latitude which has been pointed out; and this may be done accurately enough for the present purpose by a globe adjusted as above directed; for as gages, exactly in the plane of the section, were often wanting, I have used many at some small distance above and below the same, for the sake of obtaining more delineating points; and in the figure the stars at the borders which are larger than the rest are those pointed out by the gages. The intermediate parts are filled up by smaller stars arranged in straight lines between the gaged ones. The delineating points, though pretty numerous, are not so close as we might wish; it is however to be hoped that in some future time

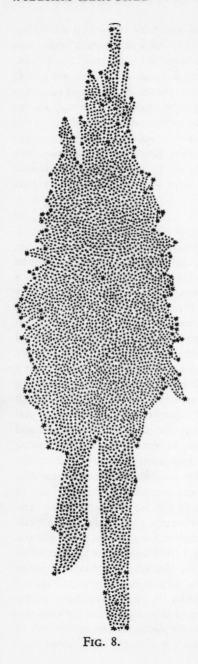

FIG. 8.

this branch of astronomy will become more cultivated, so that we may have gages for every quarter of a degree of the heavens at least, and these often repeated in the most favourable circumstances. And whenever that shall be the case, the delineations may then be repeated with all the accuracy that long experience may enable us to introduce; for, this subject being so new, I look upon what is here given partly as only an example to illustrate the spirit of the method. From this figure, however, which I hope is not a very inaccurate one, we may see that our nebula, as we observed before, is of the third form; that is: *A very extensive, branching, compound Congeries of many millions of stars*; which most probably owes its origin to many remarkably large as well as pretty closely scattered small stars, that may have drawn together the rest. Now, to have some idea of the wonderful extent of this system, I must observe that this section of it is drawn upon a scale where the distance of Sirius is no more than the 80th part of an inch;[a] so that probably all the stars, which in the finest nights we are able to distinguish with the naked eye, may be comprehended within a sphere, drawn round the large star near the middle, representing our situation in the nebula, of less than half a quarter of an inch radius.

[a] [On the scale adopted in this edition, the $\frac{1}{130}$th part of an inch.]

### The Origin of nebulous Strata.

If it were possible to distinguish between the parts of an indefinitely extended whole, the nebula we inhabit might be said to be one that has fewer marks of profound antiquity upon it than the rest. To explain this idea perhaps more clearly, we should recollect that the condensation of clusters of stars has been ascribed to a gradual approach; and whoever reflects on the numbers of ages that must have past before some of the clusters, that will be found in my intended catalogue of them, could be so far condensed as we find them at present, will not wonder if I ascribe a certain air of youth and vigour to many very regularly scattered regions of our sidereal stratum. There are moreover many places in it where there is the greatest reason to believe that the stars, if we may judge from appearances, are now drawing towards various secondary centers, and will in time separate into different clusters, so as to occasion many sub-divisions. Hence we may surmise that when a nebulous stratum consists chiefly of nebulæ of the first and second form, it probably owes its origin to what may be called the decay of a great compound nebula of the third form; and that the sub-divisions, which happened to it in length of time, occasioned all the small nebulæ which sprung from it to lie in a certain range, according as they were detached from the primary one. In like manner our system, after numbers of ages, may very possibly become divided so as to give rise to a stratum of two or three hundred nebulæ; for it would not be difficult to point out so many beginning or gathering clusters in it.[a] This view of the present subject throws a considerable light upon the appearance of that remarkable collection of many hundreds of nebulæ which are to be seen in what I have called the nebulous stratum of Coma Berenices. It appears from the extended and branching figure of our nebula, that there is room for the decomposed small nebulæ of a large, reduced, former great one to approach nearer to us in the sides than in other parts. Nay, possibly, there might originally be another very large joining branch, which in time became separated by the condensation of the stars; and this may be the reason of the little remaining breadth of our system in that very place: for the nebulæ of the stratum of the Coma are brightest and most crowded just opposite our situation, or in the pole of our system. As soon as this idea was suggested, I tried also the opposite pole, where accordingly I have met with a great number of nebulæ, though under a much more scattered form.

[a] MR. MICHELL has also considered the stars as gathered together into groups (*Phil. Trans.* vol. LVII. p. 249); which idea agrees with the sub-division of our great system here pointed out. He founds an elegant proof of this on the computation of probabilities, and mentions the Pleiades, the Præsepe Cancri, and the nebula (or cluster of stars) in the hilt of Perseus's sword, as instances.

WILLIAM HERSCHEL

### An Opening in the heavens.

Some parts of our system indeed seem already to have sustained greater ravages of time than others, if this way of expressing myself may be allowed; for instance, in the body of the Scorpion is an opening, or hole, which is probably owing to this cause. I found it while I was gaging in the parallel from 112 to 114 degrees of north polar distance. As I approached the milky way, the gages had been gradually running up from 9·7 to 17·1; when, all of a sudden, they fell down to nothing, a very few pretty large stars excepted, which made them shew 0·5, 0·7, 1·1, 1·4, 1·8; after which they again rose to 4·7, 13·5, 20·3, and soon after to 41·1. This opening is at least 4 degrees broad, but its height I have not yet ascertained. It is remarkable, that the 80th *Nébuleuse sans étoiles* of the *Connoissance des Temps*, which is one of the richest and most compressed clusters of small stars I remember to have seen, is situated just on the western border of it, and would almost authorise a suspicion that the stars, of which it is composed, were collected from that place, and had left the vacancy. What adds not a little to this surmise is, that the same phænomenon is once more repeated with the fourth cluster of stars of the *Connoissance des Temps*; which is also on the western border of another vacancy, and has moreover a small, miniature cluster, or easily resolvable nebula of about 2½ minutes in diameter, north following it, at no very great distance.[a]

### Phænomena at the Poles of our Nebula.

I ought to observe, that there is a remarkable purity or clearness in the heavens[b] when we look out of our stratum at the sides; that is, towards Leo, Virgo, and Coma Berenices, on one hand, and towards Cetus on the other; whereas the ground of the heavens becomes troubled as we approach towards the length or height of it. It was a good while before I could trace the cause of these phænomena; but since I have been acquainted with the shape of our system, it is plain that these troubled appearances, when we approach to the sides, are easily to be explained by ascribing them to some of the distant, straggling stars, that yield hardly light enough to be distinguished. And I have, indeed, often experienced this to be actually the cause, by examining these troubled spots for a long while together, when, at last, I generally perceived the stars which

[a] [The star clusters here referred to are the globular clusters M80, M4, and NGC 6144. They lie in the vicinity of an area of heavy obscuration that cuts out the light from more distant stars. The contribution of interstellar dust to the patchy distribution of stars in the Milky Way has been fully recognized only during this century.—D.]

[b] [Herschel correctly interprets an observation familiar to visual observers.—D.]

occasioned them. But when we look towards the poles of our system, where the visual ray does not graze along the side, the straggling stars of course will be very few in number; and therefore the ground of the heavens will assume that purity which I have always observed to take place in those regions.

### Enumeration of very compound Nebulæ or Milky-Ways.

As we are used to call the appearance of the heavens, where it is surrounded with a bright zone, the Milky-Way, it may not be amiss to point out some other very remarkable Nebulæ which cannot well be less, but are probably much larger than our own system; and, being also extended, the inhabitants of the planets that attend the stars which compose them must likewise perceive the same phænomena. For which reason they may also be called milky-ways by way of distinction.

My opinion of their size is grounded on the following observations. There are many round nebulæ, of the first form, of about five or six minutes in diameter, the stars of which I can see very distinctly; and on comparing them with the visual ray calculated from some of my long gages, I suppose, by the appearance of the small stars in those gages, that the centers of these round nebulæ may be 600 times the distance of Sirius from us.

In estimating the distance of such clusters I consulted rather the comparatively apparent size of the stars than their mutual distance; for the condensation in these clusters being probably much greater than in our own system, if we were to overlook this circumstance and calculate by their apparent compression, where, in about six minutes diameter, there are perhaps ten or more stars in the line of measures, we should find, that on the supposition of an equal scattering of the stars throughout all nebulæ, the distance of the center of such a cluster from us could not be less than 6000 times the distance of Sirius. And, perhaps, in putting it, by the apparent size of the stars, at 600 only, I may have considerably underrated it; but my argument, if that should be the case, will be so much the stronger. Now to proceed.

Some of these round nebulæ have others near them, perfectly similar in form, colour, and the distribution of stars, but of only half the diameter: and the stars in them seem to be doubly crowded, and only at about half the distance from each other: they are indeed so small as not to be visible without the utmost attention. I suppose these miniature nebulæ to be at double the distance of the first. An instance, equally remarkable and instructive, is a case where, in the neighbourhood of two such nebulæ as have been mentioned, I met with a third, similar, resolvable, but much smaller and fainter nebula. The stars of it are no longer to be perceived;

99

but a resemblance of colour with the former two, and its diminished size and light, may well permit us to place it at full twice the distance of the second, or about four or five times that of the first. And yet the nebulosity is not of the milky kind; nor is it so much as difficultly resolvable, or colourless. Now, in a few of the extended nebulæ, the light changes gradually so as from the resolvable to approach to the milky kind; which appears to me an indication that the milky light of nebulæ is owing to their much greater distance. A nebula, therefore, whose light is perfectly milky, cannot well be supposed to be at less than six or eight thousand times the distance of Sirius; and though the numbers here assumed are not to be taken otherwise than as very coarse estimates, yet an extended nebula, which in an oblique situation, where it is possibly fore-shortened by one-half, two-thirds, or three-fourths of its length, subtends a degree or more in diameter, cannot be otherwise than of a wonderful magnitude, and may well outvie our milky-way in grandeur.

The first I shall mention is a milky Ray of more than a degree in length. It takes $k$ (FL. 52) Cygni into its extent, to the north of which it is crookedly bent so as to be convex towards the following side; and the light of it is pretty intense. To the south of $k$ it is more diffused, less bright, and loses itself with some extension in two branches, I believe; but for want of light I could not determine this circumstance. The northern half is near two minutes broad, but the southern is not sufficiently defined to ascertain its breadth.

The next is an extremely faint milky Ray, above ¾ degree long, and 8 or 10′ broad; extended from north preceding to south following. It makes an angle of about 30 or 40 degrees with the meridian, and contains three or four places that are brighter than the rest. The stars of the Galaxy are scattered over it in the same manner as over the rest of the heavens. It follows $\varepsilon$ Cygni 11·5 minutes in time, and is 2° 19′ more south.

The third is a branching Nebulosity of about a degree and a half in right ascension, and about 48′ extent in polar distance. The following part of it is divided into several streams and windings, which, after separating, meet each other again towards the south. It precedes $\zeta$ Cygni 16′ in time, and is 1° 16′ more north. I suppose this to be joined to the preceding one; but having observed them in different sweeps, there was no opportunity of tracing their connection.[a]

[a] ["a milky Ray" (=NGC 6960), "an extremely faint milky Ray", "a branching Nebulosity". These last two are part of the same object as Herschel surmises (NGC 6992–5). The three constitute peripheral arcs of a more or less circular area of slowly expanding emission nebulosity some two and a half degrees in diameter, which is thought to be the remnants of a pre-historic supernova (the 'Veil' nebula, 'Cygnus Loops').—D.]

The fourth is a faint, extended milky Ray of about 17′ in length, and 12′ in breadth.[a] It is brightest and broadest in the middle, and the ends lose themselves. It has a small, round, very faint nebula just north of it; and also, in another place, a spot, brighter than the rest, almost detached enough to form a different nebula, but probably belonging to the great one. The Ray precedes α Trianguli 18′·8 in time, and is 55′ more north. Another observation of the same, in a finer evening, mentions its extending much farther towards the south, and that the breadth of it probably is not less than half a degree; but being shaded away by imperceptible gradations, it is difficult exactly to assign its limits.

The fifth is a Streak of light about 27′ long, and in the brightest part 3 or 4′ broad. The extent is nearly in the meridian, or a little from south preceding to north following. It follows β Ceti 5′·9 in time, and is 2° 43′ more south. The situation is so low, that it would probably appear of a much greater extent in a higher altitude.[b]

The sixth is an extensive milky Nebulosity divided into two parts; the most north being the strongest. Its extent exceeds 15′; the southern part is followed by a parcel of stars which I suppose to be the 8th of the *Connoissance des Temps*.[c]

The seventh is a wonderful, extensive Nebulosity of the milky kind. There are several stars visible in it, but they can have no connection with that nebulosity, and are, doubtless, belonging to our own system scattered before it. It is the 17th of the *Connoissance des Temps*.[d]

In the list of these must also be reckoned the beautiful Nebula of Orion.[e] Its extent is much above one degree; the eastern branch passes between two very small stars, and runs on till it meets a very bright one. Close to the four small stars, which can have no connection with the nebula, is a total blackness; and within the open part, towards the north-east, is a distinct, small, faint nebula, of an extended shape, at a distance from the border of the great one, to which it runs in a parallel

---

[a] [NGC 598, which Herschel does not seem to have realized to be M33, to which he has referred earlier. The several patches of nebulosity Herschel refers to are the brighter parts of what is really one object, a near-by, face-on Sc galaxy some 45′ in overall diameter.—D.]

[b] [NGC 247, elongated Sc galaxy.—D.]

[c] [The 'Lagoon' nebula, a bright gaseous nebulosity associated with the star cluster M8, =NGC 6523–33.—D.]

[d] [M17=NGC 6618. Gaseous nebulosity, the 'Horseshoe' or 'Omega' nebula. —D.]

[e] [Nebula of Orion, M42=NGC 1976: the finest example in the sky of gaseous nebulosity with associated stars and obscuring matter.]

direction, resembling the shoals that are seen near the coasts of some islands.

The ninth is that in the girdle of Andromeda,[a] which is undoubtedly the nearest of all the great nebulæ; its extent is above a degree and a half in length, and, in even one of the narrowest places, not less than 16' in breadth. The brightest part of it approaches to the resolvable nebulosity, and begins to shew a faint red colour; which, from many observations on the colour and magnitude of nebulæ, I believe to be an indication that its distance in this coloured part does not exceed 2000 times the distance of Sirius. There is a very considerable, broad, pretty faint, small nebula near it; my Sister discovered it August 27, 1783, with a Newtonian 2-feet sweeper. It shews the same faint colour with the great one, and is, no doubt, in the neighbourhood of it. It is not the 32d of the *Connoissance des Temps*; which is a pretty large round nebula, much condensed in the middle, and south following the great one; but this is about two-thirds of a degree north preceding it, in a line parallel to $\beta$ and $v$ Andromedæ.

To these may be added the nebula in Vulpecula:[b] for, though its appearance is not large, it is probably a double stratum of stars of a very great extent, one end whereof is turned towards us. That it is thus situated may be surmised from its containing, in different parts, nearly all the three

[a] [Andromeda nebula, M31=NGC 224. Herschel's interpretation of it as a near-by galaxy is of course correct, but he was wrong in supposing "approaching resolvability" and the distance is perhaps 300,000 times that of Sirius, not 2000. The nebula near it, discovered independently by Caroline Herschel in 1783, is NGC 205, and M32=NGC 221. Both are small elliptical galaxies close in space to the large spiral.

Herschel was a most experienced observer, and may be supposed to have been aware of the relative colours of the brighter nebulæ and the effect of his specula upon them. Some weight may be attached to his record that the brighter (i.e. nuclear) parts of M31, and the galaxy NGC 205, "shew a faint red colour". If accepted, it is one of Herschel's most remarkable observations, anticipating by a hundred and fifty years an observation that is still made visually with difficulty, but confirmed by photometry: the nuclear regions of spiral galaxies like M31 are redder than the outer parts because of the preponderance of red giant stars of Population II. The visual observation is usually attributed to Baade, using the 100-inch telescope on Mount Wilson in about 1942.—D.]

[b] [M27=NGC 6853, a large planetary nebula. Although roughly circular in shape, the distribution of light gives it its popular name of the 'Dumbbell' and accounts for Herschel's interpretation of it as a double stratum of stars seen end-on.

Note that of Herschel's nine objects listed above as type examples of "Milky Ways" like our own, *only three are galaxies!*—D.]

nebulosities; *viz.* the resolvable, the coloured but irresolvable, and a tincture of the milky kind. Now, what great length must be required to produce these effects may easily be conceived when, in all probability, our whole system, of about 800 stars in diameter, if it were seen at such a distance that one end of it might assume the resolvable nebulosity, would not, at the other end, present us with the irresolvable, much less with the colourless and milky sort of nebulosities.

### A Perforated Nebula, or Ring of Stars.

Among the curiosities of the heavens should be placed a nebula, that has a regular, concentric, dark spot in the middle, and is probably a Ring of stars.[a] It is of an oval shape, the shorter axis being to the longer as about 83 to 100; so that, if the stars form a circle, its inclination to a line drawn from the sun to the center of this nebula must be about 56 degrees. The light is of the resolvable kind, and in the northern side three very faint stars may be seen, as also one or two in the southern part. The vertices of the longer axis seem less bright and not so well defined as the rest. There are several small stars very near, but none that seem to belong to it. It is the 57th of the *Connoissance des Temps.* Fig. 9 is a representation of it.

FIG. 9.

### Planetary Nebulæ.

I shall conclude this paper with an account of a few heavenly bodies, that from their singular appearance leave me almost in doubt where to class them.[b]

The first precedes $v$ Aquarii $5' \cdot 4$ in time, and is $1'$ more north.[c] Its place, with regard to a small star Sept. 7, 1782, was, Distance $8' \ 13'' \ 51'''$; but on account of the low situation, and other unfavourable circumstances, the measure cannot be very exact. August 25, 1783, Distance $7' \ 5'' \ 11'''$, very exact, and to my satisfaction; the light being thrown in by an

[a] [M57=NGC 6720, another large planetary (gaseous) nebula, the 'Ring nebula in Lyra.—D.]

[b] [In this last section Herschel correctly classifies (by the name we use today) and describes these small gaseous nebulæ surrounding some hot stars.—D.]

[c] [NGC 7009. The "small star" is identifiable on modern photographs. The distance and position angle from the star are fixed, and the values show Herschel's observational error. Although he gives the distances to the nearest *third*, i.e. to within $\frac{1}{60}''$, the scatter in his measures is almost 4000 times greater—an example of the meaningless 'precision' of which he was sometimes guilty.—D.]

opaque-microscopic-illumination.[a] Sept. 20, 1783, Position 41° 24' south preceding the same star; very exact, and by the same kind of illumination. Oct. 17, 1783, Distance 6' 55" 7'''; a second measure 6' 56" 11''', as exact as possible. Oct. 23, 1783, Position 42° 57'; a second measure 42° 45'; single lens; power 71; opaque-microscopic-illumination. Nov. 14, 1783, Distance 7' 4" 35'''. Nov. 12, 1784, Distance 7' 22" 35'''; Position 38° 39'. Its diameter is about 10 or 15". I have examined it with the powers of 71, 227, 278, 460, and 932; and it follows the laws of magnifying, so that its body is no illusion of light. It is a little oval, and in the 7-feet reflector pretty well defined, but not sharp on the edges. In the 20-feet, of 18·7 inch aperture, it is much better defined, and has much of a planetary appearance, being all over of an uniform brightness, in which it differs from nebulæ: its light seems however to be of the starry nature, which suffers not nearly so much as the planetary disks are known to do, when much magnified.

The second of these bodies precedes the 13th of FLAMSTEED's Andromeda about 1'·6 in time, and is 22' more south.[b] It has a round, bright, pretty well defined planetary disk of about 12" diameter, and is a little elliptical. When it is viewed with a 7-feet reflector, or other inferior instruments, it is not nearly so well defined as with the 20-feet. Its situation with regard to a pretty considerable star is, Distance (with a compound glass of a low power) 7' 51" 34'''. Position 12° 0' s. preceding. Diameter taken with 278, 14" 42'''.

The third follows B (FL. 44) Ophiuchi 4'·1 in time, and is 23' more north. It is round, tolerably well defined, and pretty bright; its diameter is about 30".[c]

The fourth follows η Sagittæ 17'·1 in time, and is 2' more north. It is perfectly round, pretty bright, and pretty well defined; about ¾ min. in diameter.[d]

The fifth follows the 21st Vulpeculæ 2'·1 in time, and is 1° 46' more north. It is exactly round, of an equal light throughout, but pretty faint, and about 1' in diameter.

[a] It may be of use to explain this kind of illumination for which the Newtonian reflector is admirably constructed. On the side opposite the eye-piece an opening is to be made in the tube, through which the light may be thrown in, so as to fall on some reflecting body, or concave perforated mirror, within the eye-piece, that may throw it back upon the wires. By this means none of the direct rays can reach the eye, and those few which are reflected again from the wires do not interfere sensibly with the faintest objects, which may thus be seen undisturbed.

[b] [NGC 7662—D.]
[c] [NGC 6369—D.]
[d] [NGC 6905—D.]

The sixth precedes *h* (FL. 39) Cygni 8′·1 in time, and is 1° 26′ more south. It is perfectly round, and of an equal light, but pretty faint; its diameter is near 1′, and the edges are pretty well defined.[a]

The planetary appearance of the two first is so remarkable, that we can hardly suppose them to be nebulæ; their light is so uniform, as well as vivid, the diameters so small and well defined, as to make it almost improbable they should belong to that species of bodies. On the other hand, the effect of different powers seems to be much against their light's being of a planetary nature, since it preserves its brightness nearly in the same manner as the stars do in similar trials. If we would suppose them to be single stars with large diameters we shall find it difficult to account for their not being brighter; unless we should admit that the intrinsic light of some stars may be very much inferior to that of the generality, which however can hardly be imagined to extend to such a degree. We might suspect them to be comets about their aphelion, if the brightness as well as magnitude of the diameters did not oppose this idea; so that after all, we can hardly find any hypothesis so probable as that of their being Nebulæ; but then they must consist of stars that are compressed and accumulated in the highest degree. If it were not perhaps too hazardous to pursue a former surmise of a renewal in what I figuratively called the Laboratories of the universe, the stars forming these extraordinary nebulæ, by some decay or waste of nature, being no longer fit for their former purposes, and having their projectile forces, if any such they had, retarded in each others' atmosphere, may rush at last together, and either in succession, or by one general tremendous shock, unite into a new body. Perhaps the extraordinary and sudden blaze of a new star in Cassiopea's chair, in 1572, might possibly be of such a nature.[b] But lest I should be led too far from the path of observation, to which I am resolved to limit myself, I shall only point out a considerable use that may be made of these curious bodies. If a little attention to them should prove that, having no annual parallax,

[a] ["The fifth. . . . The sixth . . . ". The same object twice described = NGC 6894. —D.]

[b] [The "new star in Cassiopea's [sic.] chair" is the supernova of 1572 associated with the observations of Tycho Brahe. Herschel's speculations about "Laboratories of the universe", deceleration by stellar atmospheres, and stellar collisions as the source of supernovæ are astonishingly modern in outlook, though erroneous in detail. But his recognition that small bright galaxies (which at this time he thought planetary nebulæ to be) would be useful as providing an absolute reference frame against which to measure proper motions is both sound and far-seeing. The importance of the idea has been independently realized only in recent years and such work is now just beginning.—D.]

they belong most probably to the class of nebulæ, they may then be expected to keep their situation better than any one of the stars belonging to our system, on account of their being probably at a very great distance. Now to have a fixed point somewhere in the heavens, to which the motions of the rest may be referred, is certainly of considerable consequence in Astronomy; and both these bodies are bright and small enough to answer that end.

W. HERSCHEL.

Datchet near Windsor,
January 1, 1785.

# Remarks on the Construction of the Heavens[a]

Read June 11, 1789.

By the continuation of a review of the heavens with my twenty-feet reflector, I am now furnished with a second thousand of new Nebulæ.

These curious objects, not only on account of their number, but also in consideration of their great consequence, as being no less than whole sidereal systems, we may hope, will in future engage the attention of Astronomers. With a view to induce them to undertake the necessary observations, I offer them the following catalogue [not reproduced], which, like my former one, of which it is a continuation, contains a short description of each nebula or cluster of stars, as well as its situation with respect to some known object. . . .

The method I have taken of *analyzing* the heavens, if I may so express myself, is perhaps the only one by which we can arrive at a knowledge of their construction. In the prosecution of so extensive an undertaking, it may well be supposed that many things must have been suggested, by the great variety in the order, the size, and the compression of the stars, as they presented themselves to my view, which it will not be improper to communicate.

To begin our investigation according to some order, let us depart from the objects immediately around us to the most remote that our telescopes, of the greatest *power to penetrate into space*, can reach. We shall touch but slightly on things that have already been remarked.

From the earth, considered as a planet, and the moon as its satellite, we pass through the region of the rest of the planets, and their satellites. The

a [*Phil. Trans.*, LXXIX (1789), 212–26. The title of the complete paper is "Catalogue of a Second Thousand of new Nebulæ and Clusters of Stars; with a few introductory Remarks on the Construction of the Heavens".]

similarity between all these bodies is sufficiently striking to allow us to comprehend them under one general definition, of bodies not luminous in themselves, revolving round the sun. The great diminution of light, when reflected from such bodies, especially when they are also at a great distance from the light which illuminates them, precludes all possibility of following them a great way into space. But if we did not know that light diminishes as the squares of the distances encrease, and that moreover in every reflection a very considerable part is intirely lost, the motion of comets, whereby the space through which they run is measured out to us, while on their return from the sun we see them gradually disappear as they advance towards their aphelia, would be sufficient to convince us that bodies shining only with borrowed light can never be seen at any very great distance. This consideration brings us back to the sun, as a refulgent fountain of light, whilst it establishes at the same time beyond a doubt that every star must likewise be a sun, shining by its own native brightness. Here then we come to the more capital parts of the great construction.

These suns, every one of which is probably of as much consequence to a system of planets, satellites, and comets, as our own sun, are now to be considered, in their turn, as the minute parts of a proportionally greater whole. I need not repeat that by my analysis it appears, that the heavens consist of regions where the suns are gathered into separate systems, and that the catalogues I have given comprehend a list of such systems; but may we not hope that our knowledge will not stop short at the bare enumeration of phænomena capable of giving us so much instruction? Why should we be less inquisitive than the natural philosopher, who sometimes, even from an inconsiderable number of specimens of a plant, or an animal, is enabled to present us with the history of its rise, progress, and decay? Let us then compare together, and class some of these numerous sidereal groups, that we may trace the operations of natural causes as far as we can perceive their agency. The most simple form, in which we can view a sidereal system, is that of being globular. This also, very favourably to our design, is that which has presented itself most frequently, and of which I have given the greatest collection [for an example, see Plate 4].

But, first of all, it will be necessary to explain what is our idea of a cluster of stars, and by what means we have obtained it. For an instance, I shall take the phænomenon which presents itself in many clusters: It is that of a number of lucid spots, of equal lustre, scattered over a circular space, in such a manner as to appear gradually more compressed towards the middle; and which compression, in the clusters to which I allude, is generally carried so far, as, by imperceptible degrees, to end in a luminous

center, of a resolvable blaze of light.[a] To solve this appearance, it may be
conjectured, that stars of any given, very unequal magnitudes, may easily
be so arranged, in scattered, much extended, irregular rows, as to produce
the above described picture; or, that stars, scattered about almost promiscuously within the frustum of a given cone, may be assigned of such
properly diversified magnitudes as also to form the same picture. But who,
that is acquainted with the doctrine of chances, can seriously maintain such
improbable conjectures? To consider this only in a very coarse way, let us
suppose a cluster to consist of 5000 stars, and that each of them may be put
into one of 5000 given places, and have one of 5000 assigned magnitudes.
Then, without extending our calculation any further, we have five and
twenty millions of chances, out of which only one will answer the above
improbable conjecture, while all the rest are against it. When we now
remark that this relates only to the given places within the frustum of a
supposed cone, whereas these stars might have been scattered all over the
visible space of the heavens; that they might have been scattered, even
within the supposed cone, in a million of places different from the assumed
ones, the chance of this apparent cluster's not being a real one, will be
rendered so highly improbable that it ought to be intirely rejected.

Mr. MICHELL computes, with respect to the six brightest stars of the
Pleiades only, that the odds are near 500000 to 1 that no six stars, out of
the number of those which are equal in splendour to the faintest of them,
scattered at random in the whole heavens, would be within so small a
distance from each other as the Pleiades are.[b]

Taking it then for granted that the stars which appear to be gathered
together in a group are in reality thus accumulated, I proceed to prove
also that they are nearly of an equal magnitude.

The cluster itself, on account of the small angle it subtends to the eye,
we must suppose to be very far removed from us. For, were the stars
which compose it at the same distance from one another as Sirius is from
the sun; and supposing the cluster to be seen under an angle of 10 minutes,
and to contain 50 stars in one of its diameters, we should have the mean
distance of such stars twelve seconds; and therefore the distance of the
cluster from us about seventeen thousand times greater than the distance
of Sirius. Now, since the apparent magnitude of these stars is equal, and
their distance from us is also equal,—because we may safely neglect the
diameter of the cluster, which, if the center be seventeen thousand times
the distance of Sirius from us, will give us seventeen thousand and twenty-

[a] [Herschel is clearly writing here of globular clusters, and goes on to show
(correctly) that they are of truly spherical form.—D.]

[b] *Phil. Trans.* vol. LVII. p. 246 [above, p. 36].

THE CONSTRUCTION OF THE HEAVENS

five for the farthest, and seventeen thousand wanting twenty-five for the nearest star of the cluster;—it follows that we must either give up the idea of a cluster, and recur to the above refuted supposition, or admit the equality of the stars that compose these clusters. It is to be remarked that we do not mean intirely to exclude all variety of size; for the very great distance, and the consequent smallness of the component clustering stars, will not permit us to be extremely precise in the estimation of their magnitudes; though we have certainly seen enough of them to know that they are contained within pretty narrow limits; and do not, perhaps, exceed each other in magnitude more than in some such proportion as one full-grown plant of a certain species may exceed another full-grown plant of the same species.

If we have drawn proper conclusions relating to the size of stars, we may with still greater safety speak of their relative situations, and affirm that in the same distances from the center an equal scattering takes place. If this were not the case, the appearance of a cluster could not be uniformly encreasing in brightness towards the middle, but would appear nebulous in those parts which were more crowded with stars; but, as far as we can distinguish, in the clusters of which we speak, every concentric circle maintains an equal degree of compression, as long as the stars are visible; and when they become too crowded to be distinguished, an equal brightness takes place, at equal distances from the center, which is the most luminous part.

The next step in my argument will be to shew that these clusters are of a globular form. This again we rest on the sound doctrine of chances. Here, by way of strength to our argument, we may be allowed to take in all round nebulæ, though the reasons we have for believing that they consist of stars have not as yet been entered into. For, what I have to say concerning their spherical figure will equally hold good whether they be groups of stars or not. In my catalogues we have, I suppose, not less than one thousand of these round objects. Now, whatever may be the shape of a group of stars, or of a Nebula, which we would introduce instead of the spherical one, such as a cone, an ellipsis, a spheroid, a circle or a cylinder, it will be evident that out of a thousand situations, which the axes of such forms may have, there is but one that can answer the phænomenon for which we want to account; and that is, when those axes are exactly in a line drawn from the object to the place of the observer. Here again we have a million of chances of which all but one are against any other hypothesis than that which we maintain, and which, for this reason, ought to be admitted.

The last thing to be inferred from the above related appearances is, that

WILLIAM HERSCHEL

these clusters of stars are more condensed towards the center than at the surface. If there should be a group of stars in a spherical form, consisting of such as were equally scattered over all the assigned space, it would not appear to be very gradually more compressed and brighter in the middle; much less would it seem to have a bright nucleus in the center. A spherical cluster of an equal compression within,—for that such there are will be seen hereafter,—may be distinguished by the degrees of brightness which take place in going from the center to the circumference. Thus, when $a$ is the brightness in the center, it will be $\sqrt{a^2-x^2}$ at any other distance $x$ from the center. Or, putting $a=1$, and $x=$ any decimal fraction; then, in a table of natural sines, where $x$ is the sine, the brightness at $x$ will be expressed by the cosine. Now, as a gradual encrease of brightness does not agree with the degrees calculated from a supposition of an equal scattering, and as the cluster has been proved to be spherical, it must needs be admitted that there is indeed a greater accumulation towards the center. And thus, from the above-mentioned appearances, we come to know that there are globular clusters of stars nearly equal in size, which are scattered evenly at equal distances from the middle, but with an encreasing accumulation towards the center.

We may now venture to raise a superstructure upon the arguments that have been drawn from the appearance of clusters of stars and nebulæ of the form I have been examining, which is that of which I have made mention in my "*Theoretical view—Formation of Nebulæ—Form I.*"[a] It is to be remarked that when I wrote the paragraph I refer to, I delineated nature as well as I do now; but, as I there gave only a general sketch, without referring to particular cases, what I then delivered may have been looked upon as little better than hypothetical reasoning, whereas in the present instance this objection is intirely removed, since actual and particular facts are brought to vouch for the truth of every inference.

Having then established that the clusters of stars of the 1st Form, and round nebulæ, are of a spherical figure, I think myself plainly authorized to conclude that they are thus formed by the action of central powers. To manifest the validity of this inference, the figure of the earth may be given as an instance; whose rotundity, setting aside small deviations, the causes of which are well known, is without hesitation allowed to be a phænomenon decisively establishing a centipetal force. Nor do we stand in need of the revolving satellites of Jupiter, Saturn, and the Georgium Sidus [Uranus], to assure us that the same powers are likewise lodged in the masses of these planets. Their globular figure alone must be admitted as

[a] *Phil. Trans.* vol. LXXV. p. 214 [above, p. 83].

a sufficient argument to render this point uncontrovertible. We also apply this inference with equal propriety to the body of the sun, as well as to that of Mercury, Venus, Mars, and the Moon; as owing their spherical shape to the same cause. And how can we avoid inferring, that the construction of the clusters of stars, and nebulæ likewise, of which we have been speaking, is as evidently owing to central powers?

Besides, the step that I here make in my inference is in fact a very easy one, and such as ought freely to be granted. Have I not already shewn that these clusters cannot have come to their present formation by any random scattering of stars? The doctrine of chance, by exposing the very great odds against such hypotheses, may be said to demonstrate that the stars are thus assembled by some power or other. Then, what do I attempt more than merely to lead the mind to the conditions under which this power is seen to act?

In a case of such consequence I may be permitted to be a little more diffuse, and draw additional arguments from the internal construction of spherical clusters and nebulæ. If we find that there is not only a general form, which, as has been proved, is a sufficient manifestation of a centripetal force, what shall we say when the accumulated condensation, which every where follows a direction towards a center, is even visible to the very eye? Were we not already acquainted with attraction, this gradual condensation would point out a central power, by the remarkable disposition of the stars tending towards a center. In consequence of this visible accumulation, whether it may be owing to attraction only, or whether other powers may assist in the formation, we ought not to hesitate to ascribe the effect to such as are *central*; no phænomena being more decisive in that particular, than those of which I am treating.

I am fully aware of the consequences I shall draw upon myself in but mentioning other powers that might contribute to the formation of clusters. A mere hint of this kind, it will be expected, ought not to be given without sufficient foundation; but let it suffice at present to remark that my arguments cannot be affected by my terms: whether I am right to use the plural number,—central powers,—or whether I ought to say,—the known central force of gravity,—my conclusions will be equally valid. I will however add, that the idea of other central powers being concerned in the construction of the sidereal heavens, is not one that had only lately occurred to me. Long ago I have entertained a certain theory of diversified central powers of attractions and repulsions; an exposition of which I have even delivered in the years 1780, and 1781, to the Philosophical Society then existing at Bath, in several mathematical papers upon that subject. I shall, however, set aside an explanation of this theory, which would not only exceed the intended limits of this paper, but is moreover not required for what remains at present to be added, and therefore may be given some other time, when I can enter more fully into the subject of the interior construction of sidereal systems.

To return, then, to the case immediately under our present consideration, it will be sufficient that I have abundantly proved that the formation of round clusters of stars and nebulæ is either owing to central powers, or at least to one such force as refers to a center.

I shall now extend the weight of my argument, by taking in likewise every cluster of stars or nebula that shews a gradual condensation, or encreasing brightness, towards a center or certain point; whether the outward shape of such clusters or nebulæ be round, extended, or of any other given form. What has been said with regard to the doctrine of chance, will of course apply to every cluster, and more especially to the extended and irregular shaped ones, on account of their greater size: It is among these that we find the largest assemblages of stars, and most diffusive nebulosities; and therefore the odds against such assemblages happening without some particular power to gather them, encrease exceedingly with the number of the stars that are taken together. But if the gradual accumulation either of stars or encreasing brightness has before been admitted as a direction to the seat of power, the same effect will equally point out the same cause in the cases now under consideration. There are besides some additional circumstances in the appearance of extended clusters and nebulæ, that very much favour the idea of a power lodged in the brightest part. Although the form of them be not globular, it is plainly to be seen that there is a tendence towards sphericity, by the swell of the dimensions the nearer we draw towards the most luminous place, denoting as it were a course, or tide of stars, setting towards a center. And—if allegoral expressions may be allowed—it should seem as if the stars thus flocking towards the seat of power were stemmed by the crowd of those already assembled, and that while some of them are successful in forcing their predecessors sideways out of their places, others are themselves obliged to take up with lateral situations, while all of them seem equally to strive for a place in the central swelling, and generating spherical figure.

Since then almost all the nebulæ and clusters of stars I have seen, the number of which is not less than three and twenty hundred, are more condensed and brighter in the middle; and since, from every form, it is now equally apparent that the central accumulation or brightness must be the result of central powers, we may venture to affirm that this theory is no longer an unfounded hypothesis, but is fully established on grounds which cannot be overturned.

Let us endeavour to make some use of this important view of the constructing cause, which can thus model sidereal systems. Perhaps, by placing before us the very extensive and varied collection of clusters, and nebulæ furnished by my catalogues, we may be able to trace the progress of its operation, in the great laboratory of the Universe.

If these clusters and nebulæ were all of the same shape, and had the same gradual condensation, we should make but little progress in this inquiry; but, as we find so great a variety in their appearances, we shall be much sooner at a loss how to account for such various phænomena, than be in want of materials upon which to exercise our inquisitive endeavours.

Some of these round clusters consist of stars of a certain magnitude, and given degree of compression, while the whole cluster itself takes up a space of perhaps 10 minutes; others appear to be made up of stars that are much smaller, and much more compressed, when at the same time the cluster itself subtends a much smaller angle, such as 5 minutes. This diminution of the apparent size, and compression of stars, as well as diameter of the cluster to 4, 3, 2 minutes, may very consistently be ascribed to the different distances of these clusters from the place in which we observe them; in all which cases we may admit a general equality of the sizes, and compression of the stars that compose them, to take place. It is also highly probable that a continuation of such decreasing magnitudes, and encreasing compression, will justly account for the appearance of round, easily resolvable, nebulæ; where there is almost a certainty of their being clusters of stars. And no Astronomer can hesitate to go still farther, and extend his surmises by imperceptible steps to other nebulæ, that still preserve the same characteristics, with the only variations of vanishing brightness, and reduction of size.

Other clusters there are that, when they come to be compared with some of the former, seem to contain stars of an equal magnitude, while their compression appears to be considerably different. Here the supposition of their being at different distances will either not explain the apparently greater compression, or, if admitted to do this, will convey to us a very instructive consequence: which is, that the stars which are thus supposed not to be more compressed than those in the former cluster, but only to appear so on account of their greater distance, must needs be proportionally larger, since they do not appear of less magnitude than the former. As therefore, one or other of these hypotheses must be true, it is not at all improbable but that, in some instances, the stars may be more compressed; and in others, of a greater magnitude. This variety of size, in different spherical clusters, I am however inclined to believe, may not go farther than the difference in size, found among the individuals belonging to the same species of plants, or animals, in their different states of age, or vegetation, after they are come to a certain degree of growth. A farther inquiry into the circumstance of the extent, both of condensation and variety of size, that may take place with the stars of different clusters, we shall postpone till other things have been previously discussed.

Let us then continue to turn our view to the power which is moulding the different assortments of stars into spherical clusters. Any force, that acts uninterruptedly, must produce effects proportional to the time of its action. Now, as it has been shewn that the spherical figure of a cluster of stars is owing to central powers, it follows that those clusters which, *ceteris paribus*, are the most compleat in this figure, must have been the longest exposed to the action of these causes.[a] This will admit of various points of view. Suppose for instance that 5000 stars had been once in a certain scattered situation, and that other 5000 equal stars had been in the same situation, then that of the two clusters which had been longest exposed to the action of the modelling power, we suppose, would be most condensed, and more advanced to the maturity of its figure. An obvious consequence that may be drawn from this consideration is, that we are enabled to judge of the relative age, maturity, or climax of a sidereal system, from the disposition of its component parts; and, making the degrees of brightness in nebulæ stand for the different accumulation of stars in clusters, the same conclusions will extend equally to them all. But we are not to conclude from what has been said that every spherical cluster is of an equal standing in regard to absolute duration, since one that is composed of a thousand stars only, must certainly arrive to the perfection of its form sooner than another, which takes in a range of a million. Youth and age are comparative expressions; and an oak of a certain age may be called very young, while a contemporary shrub is already on the verge of its decay. The method of judging with some assurance of the condition of any sidereal system may perhaps not improperly be drawn from the standard laid down [page 110]; so that, for instance, a cluster or nebula which is very gradually more compressed

---

a [Watson made the sensible comment that Herschel's work on the age of clusters of stars "requires *stronger* premises to warrant the conclusions, especially as you do not set out with the probable primeval arrangement of Stars, but it may still serve to shew the thing hypothetically, or you might shew the Chances to be on that side. For tho' I may not be able to produce any reason why irregular clusters have not become round; it should seem you ought to shew that the previous arrange- ment in such clusters was similar to that of the globular ones & that therefore time only was required for the effect of making them globular likewise" (letter of 12 May 1789). For a note on star clusters, see above p. 70.]

and bright towards the middle, may be in the perfection of its growth, when another which approaches to the condition pointed out by a more equal compression, such as the nebulæ I have called *Planetary* seem to present us with, may be looked upon as very aged, and drawing on towards a period of change, or dissolution. This has been before surmised, when, in a former paper, I considered the uncommon degree of compression that must prevail in a nebula to give it a planetary aspect; but the argument, which is now drawn from the powers that have collected the formerly scattered stars to the form we find they have assumed, must greatly corroborate that sentiment.

This method of viewing the heavens seems to throw them into a new kind of light. They now are seen to resemble a luxuriant garden, which contains the greatest variety of productions, in different flourishing beds; and one advantage we may at least reap from it is, that we can, as it were, extend the range of our experience to an immense duration. For, to continue the simile I have borrowed from the vegetable kingdom, is it not almost the same thing, whether we live successively to witness the germination, blooming, foliage, fecundity, fading, withering, and corruption of a plant, or whether a vast number of specimens, selected from every stage through which the plant passes in the course of its existence, be brought at once to our view?

WILLIAM HERSCHEL.

Slough near Windsor, May 1, 1789.

*A Note on Herschel's copy of Wright's* An Original Theory

The explanation of the Milky Way as an optical effect due to our immersion in a disk-shaped star system is one of the best-known achievements of eighteenth-century astronomy. As we have seen, it was first proposed by Thomas Wright in *An Original Theory, or new Hypothesis of the Universe,* published in 1750, and the idea was taken up by Immanuel Kant in his *Universal Natural History and Theory of the Heavens* (1755). In his own work on the subject Herschel nowhere makes acknowledgement to either of these men, and the question arises of whether his was an independent discovery. Clearly we cannot exclude the possibility that the idea was passed on to Herschel by letter or in conversation and was remembered by him, consciously or unconsciously. But Herschel owned a copy of Wright's book, which was sold at Sotheby's in 1958 as Lot 452 of the Herschel papers and books and is now in the possession of Mr S. I. Barchas of Tucson, Arizona. Did Herschel acquire this copy *before* assembling material for his 1785 paper on the Milky Way?

On page 19 of *An Original Theory,* Wright gives the mean distance of the Sun from the Earth as 81 million miles. In the margin of Mr Barchas's copy is written "now proved to be 95 millions". This comment is in William Herschel's hand, but the writing cannot be dated except that it is of his middle rather than old age. Does the figure of 95 millions give us any clue?

In a paper published in 1788, Herschel gives the parallax of the Sun as 8"·63.[16] This is the value arrived at by Lexell in 1772,[17] and it corresponds to a distance of some 94¾ million miles—or in round figures, as Herschel gave it in 1795,[18] 95 million miles.

In a paper read to the Royal Society on 30 January 1781, but unpublished at the time, Herschel states[19] that in April 1779 he observed a Sun-spot of length 34,476 English miles; and in a paper published in 1795,[20] he tells us that on 19 April 1779 he observed a sunspot 1' 8"·06 in diameter, of length (that is, on the basis of his current value for the mean solar distance) more than 31,000 miles. The Sun-spots are evidently identical, and a calculation shows that in 1781 he was using for the mean solar distance a value of just under 104½ million miles. This is confirmed by an early notebook[21] where he gives as the distance of the Sun three times 34,761,680 miles, or again just under 104½ million miles. The corresponding solar parallax is under 8".[22] In 1782, however, Herschel gives[23] as a round figure for the angle of the Earth as seen from the Sun (that is, twice the solar parallax), 17", and not 16" or less. In other words, by 1782 he has abandoned the earlier value, and his new figure no doubt represents (in round numbers) twice Lexell's value of 8"·63, which corresponds, as we have said, to a distance of nearly 95 million miles.

Herschel's note, then, in his copy of Wright's book could (unfortunately!) have been written at any time from 1781 onwards, either before or after he began his 'gaging' of the Galaxy in the winter of 1783–84. We must therefore fall back on the fact that this is Herschel's *only* marginal note, although he annotated books extensively. In particular, the second time that Wright gives the figure of 81 million miles (page 81) it provokes no comment, suggesting that Herschel was not reading closely at this stage. This would be entirely consistent with his usual attitude to astronomical speculators. Thus in discussing solar motion in 1805 he writes, "Those who like to indulge in fanciful reviews of the heavens, might easily build a system upon hypotheses not altogether without some plausibility in their favour. Accordingly we find that Mr Lambert, in a work which is full of the most fantastic imaginations. . . ."[24] This, coupled with Herschel's usual care in making acknowledgements, suggests that he glanced through Wright's book when his own studies on the Galaxy were well advanced, expecting to learn little from it, and that his expectations were fulfilled.

# Chapter Four

# The Construction of the Heavens: true nebulosity and the second synthesis

WITH the elaboration of his conception of nebulæ as collections of stars developing and clustering under the action of attractive powers, it seemed as though the outlines of Herschel's theory of 'the construction of the heavens' were complete. But at least two pieces of the jigsaw puzzle refused to fall into place. First, there was the difficulty of explaining the more extensive examples of nebulosity, in particular the famous nebula in Orion (which is a relatively near gaseous cloud). In 1785 Herschel had suggested that it was a distant star system which "may well outvie our milky-way in grandeur" (above, p. 100), but it was really too extensive for him to be entirely happy with this explanation (below, p. 126). In addition, many astronomers believed they had observed major changes in the nebula.[1] Herschel was to write in 1802, "The changes I have observed in the great milky nebulosity of Orion, 23 years ago, and which have also been noticed by other astronomers, cannot permit us to look upon this phenomenon as arising from immensely distant regions of fixed stars",[2] and others independently arrived at the same conclusion.[3] Yet oddly enough the nebula does not in fact alter so strikingly, so that we have an example of erroneous observations leading to a correct result.

Secondly, there was the problem of planetary nebulæ, which we have seen worrying him in both the 1785 and the 1789 papers (above, pp. 103–6, 115)—"heavenly bodies, that from their singular appearance leave me almost in doubt where to class them". As it happened, what finally convinced him of the existence of "true nebulosity" was a particularly symmetrical planetary nebula which he observed on 13 November 1790. The announcement that he no longer equated nebulæ with star systems came a few weeks later.

## On Nebulous Stars, properly so called[a]

Read February 10, 1791.

IN one of my late examinations of a space in the heavens, which I had not reviewed before, I discovered *a star of about the 8th magnitude, surrounded with a faintly luminous atmosphere, of a considerable extent.*[b] The phænomenon was so striking that I could not help reflecting upon the circumstances that attended it, which appeared to me to be of a very instructive nature, and such as may lead to inferences which will throw a considerable light on some points relating to the construction of the heavens.

Cloudy or nebulous stars have been mentioned by several astronomers; but this name ought not to be applied to the objects which they have pointed out as such; for, on examination, they proved to be either mere clusters of stars, plainly to be distinguished with my large instruments, or such nebulous appearances as might be reasonably supposed to be occasioned by a multitude of stars at a vast distance. The milky way itself, as I have shewn in some former Papers, consists intirely of stars, and by imperceptible degrees I have been led on from the most evident congeries of stars to other groups in which the lucid points were smaller, but still very plainly to be seen; and from them to such wherein they could but barely be suspected, till I arrived at last to spots in which no trace of a star was to be discerned. But then the gradations to these latter were by such well-connected steps as left no room for doubt but that all these phæno-

---

[a] [*Phil. Trans.*, LXXXI (1791), 71–88.]

[b] [This object Herschel identifies as his IV. 69=NGC 1514: a planetary nebula, see note at foot of page 120.—D.]

mena were equally occasioned by stars, variously dispersed in the immense expanse of the universe.

When I pursued these researches, I was in the situation of a natural philosopher who follows the various species of animals and insects from the height of their perfection down to the lowest ebb of life; when, arriving at the vegetable kingdom, he can scarcely point out to us the precise boundary where the animal ceases and the plant begins; and may even go so far as to suspect them not to be essentially different. But recollecting himself, he compares, for instance, one of the human species to a tree, and all doubt upon the subject vanishes before him. In the same manner we pass through gentle steps from a coarse cluster of stars, such as the Pleiades, the Præsepe, the milky way, the cluster in the Crab,[a] the nebula in Hercules,[b] that near the preceding hip of Bootes,[c] the 17th, 38th, 41st of the 7th class of my Catalogues, the 10th, 20th, 35th of the 6th class, the 33d, 48th, 213th of the 1st, the 12th, 150th, 756th of the 2d, and the 18th, 140th, 725th of the 3d, without any hesitation, till we find ourselves brought to an object such as the nebula in Orion, where we are still inclined to remain in the once adopted idea, of stars exceedingly remote, and inconceivably crowded, as being the occasion of that remarkable appearance.[d] It seems, therefore, to require a more dissimilar object

[a] ["the cluster in the Crab": probably M67 = NGC 2682, to which Herschel has referred earlier (p. 81) as part of the "stratum of Cancer".—D.]

[b] ["nebula in Hercules", M13 = NGC 6205, a globular cluster.—D.]

[c] ["that near the preceding hip of Bootes", M3 = NGC 5272, a globular cluster. —D.]

[d] ["the 7th class of my Catalogues". These classes are not to be confused with the *Forms* of nebulæ, of which Herschel writes on p. 83. In his catalogues Herschel gives an object an arabic number in one of eight classes designated by Roman numerals. These *Classes* are:

| I | Bright nebulæ | V | Very large nebulæ |
|---|---|---|---|
| II | Faint nebulæ | VI | Very condensed and rich clusters of stars |
| III | Very faint nebulæ | VII | Compressed clusters of small and large stars |
| IV | Planetary nebulæ | VIII | Coarsely scattered clusters of stars |

| H. VII. | 17 | = NGC 2362 | Galactic cluster (H. = Herschel catalogue) |
|---|---|---|---|
| | 38 | 2324 | Galactic cluster |
| | 41 | 7296 | Galactic cluster |
| H. VI. | 10 | 6144 | Globular cluster |
| | 20 | 288 | Globular cluster |
| | 35 | 136 | Small compact galactic cluster |
| H. I. | 33 | 4124 | Galaxy |
| | 48 | 6356 | Globular cluster |
| | 213 | 4449 | Bright elongated galaxy, Type Irr 1 |

to set us right again. A glance like that of the naturalist, who casts his eye from the perfect animal to the perfect vegetable, is wanting to remove the veil from the mind of the astronomer. The object I have mentioned above, is the phænomenon that was wanting for this purpose. View, for instance, the 19th cluster of my 6th class,[a] and afterwards cast your eye on this cloudy star,[b] and the result will be no less decisive than that of the naturalist we have alluded to. Our judgement, I may venture to say, will be, that *the nebulosity about the star is not of a starry nature.*

But, that we may not be too precipitate in these new decisions, let us enter more at large into the various grounds which induced us formerly to surmise, that every visible object, in the extended and distant heavens, was of the starry kind, and collate them with those which now offer themselves for the contrary opinion.

It has been observed, on a former occasion, that all the smaller parts of other great systems, such as the planets, their rings and satellites, the comets, and such other bodies of the like nature as may belong to them, can never be perceived by us, on account of the faintness of light reflected from small, opaque objects; in my present remarks, therefore, all these are to be intirely set aside.

A well connected series of objects, such as we have mentioned above, has led us to infer, that all nebulæ consist of stars. This being admitted, we were authorized to extend our analogical way of reasoning a little farther. Many of the nebulæ had no other appearance than that whitish cloudiness, on the blue ground upon which they seemed to be projected; and why

| H. II. 12 | =NGC 4651 | Galaxy |
|---|---|---|
| 150 | 5645 | Galaxy, Irr |
| 756 | 5820 | Galaxy, So |
| H. III. 18 | 4505 | (identity doubtful, probably=NGC 4496) Galaxy |
| 140 | 6064 | (identity doubtful, probably=NGC 6052) Galaxy |
| 725 | 4242 | Galaxy |

Note here the *order* in which Herschel arranges his objects, from open clusters like the Pleiades through classes 7, 6, 1, 2, to 3, ending with the Orion nebula which he still believes to be made of stars "exceedingly remote, and inconceivably crowded". (In footnotes, not reproduced, Herschel gives the positions of these nebulæ.)—D.]

[a] [H. VI. 19=NGC 5897, a globular cluster—D.]

[b] ["this cloudy star". The key object of this paper. Herschel gives its position later in the paper; its identification is H. IV. 69=NGC 1514. It is a planetary nebula, measuring about $2' \times 1'.5$, with a fairly conspicuous central star of $9^{m}.7$. The surface brightness of the nebulosity is smaller, and the central star relatively more prominent, than is usual in planetary nebulæ. (See Plate 5.)—D.]

the same cause should not be assigned to explain the most extensive nebulosities, as well as those that amounted only to a few minutes of a degree in size, did not appear. It could not be inconsistent to call up a telescopic milky way, at an immense distance, to account for such phænomena; and if any part of the nebulosity seemed detached from the rest, or contained a visible star or two, the probability of seeing a few near stars, apparently scattered over the far distant regions of myriads of sidereal collections, rendered nebulous by their distance, would also clear up these singularities.

In order to be more easily understood in my remarks on the comparative disposition of the heavenly bodies, I shall mention some of the particulars which introduced the ideas of *connection* and *disjunction*: for these, being properly founded upon an examination of objects that may be reviewed at any time, will be of considerable importance to the validity of what we may advance with regard to my lately discovered nebulous stars.

On June the 27th, 1786, I saw a beautiful cluster of very small stars of various sizes, about 15′ in diameter, and very rich of stars.[a] On viewing this object, it is impossible to withhold our assent to the idea which occurs, that these stars are connected so far one with another as to be gathered together, within a certain space, of little extent, when compared to the vast expanse of the heavens. As this phænomenon has been repeatedly seen in a thousand cases, I may justly lay great stress on the idea of such stars being connected.

In the year 1779, the 9th of September, I discovered a very small star near ε Bootis.[b] The question here occurring, whether it had any connection with ε or not, was determined in the negative; for, considering the number of stars scattered in a variety of places, it is very far from being uncommon, that a star at a great distance should happen to be nearly in a line drawn from the sun through ε, and thus constitute the observed double star.

The 7th of September, 1782, when I first saw the planetary nebula near ν Aquarii,[c] I pronounced it to be a system whose parts were connected together. Without entering into any kind of calculation, it is evident, that a certain equal degree of light within a very small space, joined to the particular shape this object presents to us, which is nearly round, and even in its deviation consistent with regularity, being a little elliptical, ought naturally to give us the idea of a conjunction in the things

[a] [H. VI. 23 = NGC 6645, a galactic cluster—D.]
[b] *Phil. Trans.* Vol. LXXII. p. 115. Catalogue of Double Stars, I. 1.
[c] [H. IV. 1 = NGC 7009, planetary nebula correctly described by Herschel—D.]

that produce it. And a considerable addition to this argument may be derived from a repetition of the same phænomenon, in nine or ten more of a similar construction.

When I examined the cluster of stars, following the head of the great dog,[a] I found on the 19th of March, 1786, that there was within this cluster a round, resolvable nebula, of about two minutes in diameter, and nearly of an equal degree of light throughout.[b] Here, considering that the cluster was free from nebulosity in other parts, and that many such clusters, as well as many such nebulæ, exist in divers parts of the heavens, it appeared to me very probable, that the nebula was unconnected with the cluster; and that a similar reason would as easily account for this appearance as it had resolved the phænomenon of the double star near ε Bootis; that is, a casual situation of our sun and the two other objects nearly in a line. And though it may be rather more remarkable, that this should happen with two compound systems, which are not by far so numerous as single stars, we have, to make up for this singularity, a much larger space in which it may take place, the cluster being of a very considerable extent.

On the 15th of February, 1786, I discovered that one of my planetary nebulæ,[c] had a spot in the center, which was more luminous than the rest, and with long attention, a very bright, round, well defined center became visible. I remained not a single moment in doubt, but that the bright center was connected with the rest of the apparent disk.

In the year 1785, the 6th of October, I found a very bright, round nebula, of about 1½ minute in diameter.[d] It has a large, bright nucleus in the middle, which is undoubtedly connected with the luminous parts about it. And though we must confess, that if this phænomenon, and many more of the same nature, recorded in my catalogues of nebulæ, consist of clustering stars, we find ourselves involved in some difficulty to account for the extraordinary condensation of them about the center; yet the idea of a connection between the outward parts and these very condensed ones within is by no means lessened on that account.

There is a telescopic milky way, which I have traced out in the heavens in many sweeps made from the year 1783 to 1789.[e] It takes up a space of

[a] [M46=NGC 2437, galactic cluster in Canis Major—D.]

[b] [H. IV. 39=NGC 2438, planetary nebula involved in M46—D.]

[c] [H. IV. 37=NGC 6543, planetary nebula—D.]

[d] [H. I. 107=NGC 1407, a galaxy of type E0 with a pronounced bright nucleus—a not unusual feature of galaxies.—D.]

[e] R.A. from 5 h. 15' 8" to 5 h. 39' 1". P.D. from 87° 46' to 98° 10'.

[The area described by H. is extended N.-S. and includes the Orion nebula and more than 60 square degrees of the heavens, and there are thousands of stars scattered over it: among others, four that form a trapezium, and are situated in the well known nebula of Orion, which is included in the above extent. All these stars, as well as the four I have mentioned, I take to be intirely unconnected with the nebulosity which involves them in appearance. Among them is also *d* Orionis, a cloudy star, improperly so called[a] by former astronomers; but it does not seem to be connected with the milkiness any more than the rest.

I come now to some other phænomena, that, from their singularity, merit undoubtedly a very full discussion. Among the reasons which induced us to embrace the opinion, that all very faint milky nebulosity ought to be ascribed to an assemblage of stars is, that we could not easily assign any other cause of sufficient importance for such luminous appearances, to reach us at the immense distance we must suppose ourselves to be from them. But if an argument of considerable force should now be brought forward, to shew the existence of a luminous matter, in a state of modification very different from the construction of a sun or star, all objections, drawn from our incapacity of accounting for new phænomena upon old principles, will lose their validity.

Hitherto I have been shewing, by various instances in objects whose places are given, in what manner we may form the ideas of connection and its contrary by an attentive inspection of them only: I will now relate a series of observations, with remarks upon them as they are delivered, from which I shall afterwards draw a few simple conclusions, that seem to be of considerable importance.

To distinguish the observations from the remarks, the former are given in italics, and the date annexed is that on which the objects were discovered; but the descriptions are extracted from all the observations that have been made upon them.

*October 16, 1784. A star of about the 9th magnitude, surrounded by a milky nebulosity, or chevelure, of about 3 minutes in diameter. The nebulosity is very faint, and a little extended or elliptical, the extent being not far from the meridian, or a little from north preceding to south following. The chevelure involves a small*

the three stars of Orion's Belt. The area is in the Milky Way, rich in nebulosity and highly luminous stars of types O and B, but there are no features defining its boundary which would justify Herschel's very accurate specification of its limits in R.A. and Dec. We now know that for the greater part the stars and gas in such regions are physically associated.—D.]

[a] [*d* Orionis "a cloudy star, improperly so called", =49 Ori=BD−7°1142. There are very faint gaseous nebulæ in the vicinity, including IC430, but if Herschel did not see them, certainly his predecessors could not have done.—D.]

*star, which is about 1½ minute north of the cloudy star; other stars of equal magnitude are perfectly free from this appearance.*[a]

My present judgement concerning this remarkable object is, that the nebulosity belongs to the star which is situated in its center. The small one, on the contrary, which is mentioned as involved, being one of many that are profusely scattered over this rich neighbourhood, I suppose to be quite unconnected with this phænomenon. A circle of three minutes in diameter is sufficiently large to admit another small star, without any bias to the judgement I form concerning the one in question.

It must appear singular, that such an object should not have immediately suggested all the remarks contained in this Paper; but about things that appear new we ought not to form opinions too hastily, and my observations on the construction of the heavens were then but entered upon. In this case, therefore, it was the safest way to lay down a rule not to reason upon the phænomena that might offer themselves, till I should be in possession of a sufficient stock of materials to guide my researches. . . .

January the 6th, 1785. *A bright star with a considerable milky chevelure; a little extended, 4 or 5' in length, and near 4' broad; it loses itself insensibly. Other stars of equal magnitude are perfectly free from this chevelure.*[b]

The connection between the star and the chevelure cannot be doubted, from the insensible gradation of its luminous appearance, decreasing as it receded from the center. . . .

November 13, 1790. *A most singular phænomenon! A star of about the 8th magnitude, with a faint luminous atmosphere, of a circular form, and of about 3' in diameter. The star is perfectly in the center, and the atmosphere is so diluted, faint, and equal throughout, that there can be no surmise of its consisting of stars; nor can there be a doubt of the evident connection between the atmosphere and the star. Another star not much less in brightness, and in the same field with the above, was perfectly free from any such appearance.*[c]

This last object is so decisive in every particular, that we need not

[a] [H. IV. 19=NGC 2170. Not a planetary nebula, but a star embedded in irregular galactic nebulosity, probably partly reflection nebulosity.]

[b] [H. IV. 24=NGC 2023. A star embedded in a small bright patch of gaseous nebulosity, in an area following the well-known 'Horse Head' dark nebula S. of ζ Orionis. In this section of his paper Herschel describes some dozen objects as examples of nebulous stars he has seen in his sweeps: this one only is given here, as an example. For the greater part he chooses correctly either planetary nebulæ, or stars involved in small patches of galactic nebulosity. Many of the latter are in Orion and Monoceros, regions containing many such objects. In a few cases Herschel errs and describes a galaxy with a bright nucleus or a foreground star.—D.]

[c] [NGC 1514. See note ([b]) on p. 120, and Plate 5.—D.]

hesitate to admit it as a pattern, from which we are authorized to draw the following important consequences.

Supposing the connection between the star and its surrounding nebulosity to be allowed, we argue, that one of the two following cases must necessarily be admitted. In the first place, if the nebulosity consist of stars that are very remote, which appear nebulous on account of the small angles their mutual distances subtend at the eye, whereby they will not only, as it were, run into one another, but also appear extremely faint and diluted; then, what must be the enormous size of the central point, which outshines all the rest in so superlative a degree as to admit of no comparison? In the next place, if the star be no bigger than common, how very small and compressed must be those other luminous points that are the occasion of the nebulosity which surrounds the central one? As, by the former supposition, the luminous central point must far exceed the standard of what we call a star, so, in the latter, the shining matter about the center will be much too small to come under the same denomination; we therefore either have a central body which is not a star, or have a star which is involved in a shining fluid, of a nature totally unknown to us.

I can adopt no other sentiment than the latter, since the probability is certainly not for the existence of so enormous a body as would be required to shine like a star of the 8th magnitude, at a distance sufficiently great to cause a vast system of stars to put on the appearance of a very diluted, milky nebulosity.

But what a field of novelty is here opened to our conceptions! A shining fluid, of a brightness sufficient to reach us from the remote regions of a star of the 8th, 9th, 10th, 11th, or 12th magnitude, and of an extent so considerable as to take up 3, 4, 5, or 6 minutes in diameter! Can we compare it to the coruscations of the electrical fluid in the aurora borealis? Or to the more magnificent cone of the zodiacal light as we see it in spring or autumn? The latter, notwithstanding I have observed it to reach at least 90 degrees from the sun, is yet of so little extent and brightness as probably not to be perceived even by the inhabitants of Saturn or the Georgian planet [Uranus], and must be utterly invisible at the remoteness of the nearest fixed star.

More extensive views may be derived from this proof of the existence of a shining matter. Perhaps it has been too hastily surmised that all milky nebulosity, of which there is so much in the heavens, is owing to starlight only. These nebulous stars may serve as a clue to unravel other mysterious phænomena. If the shining fluid that surrounds them is not so essentially connected with these nebulous stars but that it can also exist without them, which seems to be sufficiently probable, and will be examined hereafter, we may with great facility explain that very extensive, telescopic nebulosity, which, as I mentioned before, is expanded over more than sixty degrees of the heavens, about the constellation of Orion; a luminous matter accounting much better for it than clustering stars at a distance. In this case we may also pretty nearly guess at its situation, which must commence somewhere about the range of the stars of the 7th magnitude, or a little farther from us, and extend unequally in some places perhaps to the regions of those of the 9th, 10th, 11th, and 12th. The foundation for this surmise is, that, not unlikely, some of the stars that happen to be situated in a more condensed part of it, or that perhaps by their own attraction draw together some quantity of this fluid greater than what they are intitled to by their situation in it, will, of course, assume the appearance of cloudy stars; and many of those I have named are either in this stratum of luminous matter, or very near it.

We have said above, that in nebulous stars the existence of the shining fluid does not seem to be so essentially connected with the central points that it might not also exist without them. For this opinion we may assign several reasons. One of them is the great resemblance between the chevelure of these stars and the diffused extensive nebulosity mentioned before, which renders it highly probable that they are of the same nature. Now, if this be admitted, the separate existence of the luminous matter, or its independance on a central star, is fully proved. We may also judge, very confidently, that the light of this shining fluid is no kind of reflection from the star in the center; for, as we have already observed, reflected light could never reach us at the great distance we are from such objects.[a] Besides, how impenetrable would be an atmosphere of a sufficient density to reflect so great a quantity of light? And yet we observe, that the outward parts of the chevelure are nearly as bright as those that are close to the star; so that this supposed atmosphere ought to give no obstruction to the passage of the central rays. If, therefore, this matter is self-luminous, it seems more fit to produce a star by its condensation than to depend on the star for its existence.

Many other diffused nebulosities, besides that about the constellation of Orion, have been observed or suspected; but some of them are probably very distant, and run out far into space. For instance, about 5 minutes in

[a] [Herschel has correctly asserted in the preceding paragraph but one that the zodiacal light would be invisible from the nearest star. But here he is incorrect: a few *reflection nebulæ* are known, around highly luminous stars, the light of which is starlight reflected from interstellar particles. Even in the commoner gaseous nebulæ the gas is not of course truly self-luminous, but derives its energy from the ultra-violet light of near-by stars, or from collisional processes.—D.]

time preceding $\xi$ Cygni, I suspect as much of it as covers near four square degrees;[a] and much about the same quantity 44' preceding the 125 Tauri.[b] A space of almost 8 square degrees, 6' preceding $\alpha$ Trianguli, seems to be tinged with milky nebulosity.[c] Three minutes preceding the 46 Eridani, strong, milky nebulosity is expanded over more than two square degrees.[d] 54' preceding the 13th Canum venaticorum, and again 48' preceding the same star,[e] I found the field of view affected with whitish nebulosity throughout the whole breadth of the sweep, which was 2° 39'. 4' following the 57 Cygni, a considerable space is filled with faint, milky nebulosity, which is pretty bright in some places, and contains the 37th nebula of my Vth class, in the brightest part of it.[f] In the neighbourhood of the 44th Piscium, very faint nebulosity appears to be diffused over more than 9 square degrees of the heavens.[g] Now, all these phænomena, as we have already seen, will admit of a much easier explanation by a luminous fluid than by stars at an immense distance.[h]

The nature of planetary nebulæ, which has hitherto been involved in much darkness, may now be explained with some degree of satisfaction, since the uniform and very considerable brightness of their apparent disk accords remarkably well with a much condensed, luminous fluid; whereas to suppose them to consist of clustering stars will not so completely

[a] [$5^m$p.$\xi$ Cygni. The North America nebula=NGC 7000, see note ($^f$) below. —D.]

[b] [$44^m$p. 125 Tauri. The region of the galactic nebulosity IC 2087 is $60^m$p; Herschel's area, following an obscured region, does not show any nebulosity.—D.]

[c] [$6^m$p.$\alpha$ Trianguli. M33 (bright, large galaxy) is $18^m$p, no other nebulosity.—D.]

[d] [$3^m$p. 46 Eridani. The excessively faint nebulosity in this area could not have been seen visually.—D.]

[e] [$54^m$p. 13 Canum venaticorum. This star is now designated 31 Com. Ber. The field is devoid of nebulosity.—D.]

[f] [$4^m$f. 57 Cygni. The same field described a few lines earlier as $5^m$p. $\xi$ Cygni. This is the so-called "North America" nebula (diffuse gaseous), from its shape. Notoriously difficult to see visually, though photographed easily, Herschel's description of it as "pretty bright in some places", as seen with a speculum metal mirror of long focus, testifies to his visual acuity.—D.]

[g] [Neighbourhood of 44 Piscium. No nebulosity exists here: the field is in the ecliptic and Herschel may conceivably have seen the zodiacal band.—D.]

[h] [For the greater part it is difficult to understand these six examples of "fields affected with whitish nebulosity" (for further puzzling examples, see note ($^c$) on p. 136). Except for that of the North America nebula the fields are not distinguished by any remarkable nebulosity, or are actually quite free from any. There are much better examples of the phenomenon in areas of the Milky Way, with which Herschel must have been familiar.—D.]

account for the milkiness or soft tint of their light, to produce which it would be required that the condensation of the stars should be carried to an almost inconceivable degree of accumulation. The surmise of the regeneration of stars, by means of planetary nebulæ, expressed in a former Paper, will become more probable, as all the luminous matter contained in one of them, when gathered together into a body of the size of a star, would have nearly such a quantity of light as we find the planetary nebulæ to give. To prove this experimentally, we may view them with a telescope that does not magnify sufficiently to shew their extent, by which means we shall gather all their light together into a point, when they will be found to assume the appearance of small stars; that is, of stars at the distance of those which we call of the 8th, 9th, or 10th magnitude. Indeed this idea is greatly supported by the discovery of a well defined, lucid point, resembling a star, in the center of one of them: for the argument which has been used, in the case of nebulous stars, to shew the probability of the existence of a luminous matter, which rested upon the disparity between a bright point and its surrounding shining fluid, may here be alleged with equal justice. If the point be a generating star, the further accumulation of the already much condensed, luminous matter, may complete it in time.

How far the light that is perpetually emitted from millions of suns may be concerned in this shining fluid, it might be presumptuous to attempt to determine; but, notwithstanding the unconceivable subtilty of the particles of light, when the number of the emitting bodies is almost infinitely great, and the time of the continual emission indefinitely long, the quantity of emitted particles may well become adequate to the constitution of a shining fluid, or luminous matter, provided a cause can be found that may retain them from flying off, or reunite them. But such a cause cannot be difficult to guess at, when we know that light is so easily reflected, refracted, inflected, and deflected; and that, in the immense range of its course, it must pass through innumerable systems, where it cannot but frequently meet with many obstacles to its rectilinear progression. Not to mention the great counteraction of the united attractive force of whole sidereal systems, which must be continually exerting their power upon the particles while they are endeavouring to fly off. However, we shall lay no stress upon a surmise of this kind, as the means of verifying it are wanting: nor is it of any immediate consequence to us to know the origin of the luminous matter. Let it suffice, that its existence is rendered evident, by means of nebulous stars.

I hope it will be found, that in what has been said I have not launched out into hypothetical reasonings; and that facts have all along been kept sufficiently in view. But, in order to give every one a fair opportunity to follow me in the reflections I have been led into, the place of every object from which I have argued has been purposely added, that the validity of what I have advanced might be put to the proof by those who are inclined, and furnished with the necessary instruments to undertake an attentive and repeated inspection of the same phænomena.

W. HERSCHEL.

Slough, Jan. 1, 1791.

Already Herschel's mind was extending his theory of the development of star clusters under attractive forces to include true nebulosity, as we see from the brief hint in this paper: "If therefore, this matter is self-luminous, it seems more fit to produce a star by its condensation than to depend on the star for its existence."

His next publication on the subject was the preface written in 1802 to his third and last catalogue of nebulæ and star clusters[4] and containing "Remarks on the construction of the heavens". The catalogue itself continued the classification scheme of earlier catalogues, which "is little more than an arrangement of the objects for the convenience of the observer, and may be compared to the disposition of the books in a library, where the different sizes of the volumes is often more considered than their contents".[5] Herschel proposed in the preface to give "an enumeration of the species" of objects seen in the heavens, "and leave a particular examination of the separate divisions, for some early future occasions".

He considers first single stars, double stars, and systems of multiple stars; then "clustering stars, and the milky-way", groups of stars, and clusters of stars (that is, globular clusters); and finally nebulæ, "stars with burs, or stellar nebulæ", "milky nebulosity", "nebulous stars", "planetary nebulæ", and "planetary nebulæ with centres". The writing lacks his usual assurance, although he is now able to subdivide "milky nebulosity" into two different kinds, "one of them being deceptive, namely, such as arises from widely extended regions of closely connected clustering stars, contiguous to each other, like the collections that construct our milky-way. The other, on the contrary, being real, and possibly at no very great distance from us", instancing the nebula in Orion as an example of the latter.[6] The finest passage in the paper occurs when Herschel translates into light-years the calculation of distances he had published in an earlier paper (below, p. 167), drawing the corollary fundamental to modern cosmology

> that a telescope with a power of penetrating into space, like my 40-feet one, has also, as it may be called, a power of penetrating into time past. To explain this, we must consider that, from the known velocity of light, it may be proved, that when we look at Sirius, the rays which enter the eye cannot have been less than 6 years and $4\frac{1}{2}$ months coming from that star to the observer [the correct figure is 8·7 years]. Hence it follows, that when we see an object of the calculated distance at which one of these very remote nebulæ may still be perceived, the rays of light which convey its image to the eye, must have been more than nineteen hundred and ten thousand, that is, almost two millions of years on their way; and that, consequently, so many years ago, this object must already have had an existence in the sidereal heavens, in order to send out those rays by which we now perceive it.[7]

And there the matter rested until Herschel was well into his seventies. His second and final theory of the development of 'nebulæ and star clusters' under the action of attractive forces was published in two papers (reproduced in part, below, pp. 133–62), one appearing in 1811 and the other in 1814. Whereas before he had believed himself to be dealing only with star systems, now he had to consider both nebulosity and star systems. This meant explaining how nebulosity develops with time, how it finally changes into stars, and how these stars then develop into highly condensed clusters. The importance of the temporal dimension in his theory increases accordingly, whereas the spatial distribution of nebulæ and clusters is now significant in so far as it offers clues to their development in time.

Herschel (so to speak) takes the two and a half thousand members of his catalogues, labels each according to what he believes to be its age and then lays them out for our inspection in order of supposed increasing maturity. "It will be found that those contained in one article, are so closely allied to those in the next, that there is perhaps not so much difference between them, if I may use the comparison, as there would be in an annual description of the human figure, were it given from the birth of a child till he comes to be a man in his prime" (below, p. 135).

Once again Herschel is forcing very different objects into a single sequence and hopelessly over-simplifying the processes at work. This no doubt is to be expected in the infancy of a major problem. But whereas before there was a complex theoretical structure into which Herschel's observations could be fitted—with distance determined by resolvability, age by the approach to globular form, and spatial distribution by the initial near-uniformity—now the theoretical elements are few and uncertain. In particular, an unresolved object may be a near-by nebulosity or a distant star cluster or galaxy, and there is no obvious way of distinguishing these possibilities. Even the great Andromeda nebula, previously and rightly compared to our own Galaxy, now becomes an ambiguous object (p. 156).

In fact, as the astrophysical notes show, most of the objects Herschel describes in the 1811 paper are after all complete galaxies; and yet Herschel appears to regard each object as condensing to form, not a multitude of stars, but one, or at most a few. Some condense to become a mere comet—and Laplace himself wrote to say that his own ideas agree marvellously with Herschel's, for he too thinks that suns were once large nebulæ, and comets small ones![8]

On the other hand, fundamental elements of his synthesis— the evolution of star clusters, the formation of stars from 'nebulosity'—are very much alive today. By amassing the natural history of nebulæ and star clusters Herschel provided for the first time the observational raw material; by his theoretical interpretation of this evidence, vulnerable though it was proving to be, he led the way in raising their study to the status of scientific theory.

Many years, however, were to pass before Herschel's ideas were to be developed on any scale, and this fact, surprising at first sight, has been explained by his granddaughter as due to the clerical influence in British astronomy. "Under these circumstances", she writes, "it was natural that there was a certain reluctance to show approval of Herschel's theories, which seemed to run counter to the accepted interpretation of the Biblical account of Creation."[9] This statement has been quoted so often as established fact that it is worth remarking that Lady Lubbock cites no evidence in support of her hypothesis, nor does any seem to have been forthcoming in the thirty years since her book was published. Most English astronomical works of the early nineteenth century are either purely scientific or written from a theistic rather than strictly Christian standpoint. One author who does touch on the wider implications of Herschel's work is T. Dick, author of *The Christian Philosopher*, who in *The Sidereal Heavens, and other subjects connected with astronomy, as illustrative of the character of the deity, and of an infinity of worlds* (1840) wrote, "It is an opinion now very generally entertained, that the self-luminous matter to which we refer is the chaotic materials out of which new suns or worlds may be formed. . . . Nor do we conceive that this hypothesis is inconsistent with what we know of the attributes and operations of the Almighty. . . . All that we require on this point is some more direct and decisive proofs of the validity of the hypothesis we are now considering."[10] As this last sentence suggests, to explain the apparent neglect of Herschel's cosmogonical papers we need not go outside astronomy. In 1847, when William Parsons's giant telescope with its 6-foot mirror was barely completed, F. G. W. Struve could write "L'étude de ciel nébuleux paraît être le domaine presque exclusif des Herschel",[11] for only William and John had both the instruments and the dogged persistence necessary in this field. As for William's theorizing, with one voice astronomers demanded time in which to amass observations and observe the alleged changes actually taking place. Not for them the interpretation of static evidence to reveal dynamic processes. How, asks John Herschel himself, is one to make the step from "observed graduation" to "concluding them [the nebulæ and star clusters] to be in a course of progress from one state in the series to another"? "So wide is the field of conjecture, and so uncertain the analogies we have to guide us, that we shall do well for the present to dismiss hypothesis, and have recourse (perhaps for centuries to come) to observation."[12]

## Astronomical Observations relating to the Construction of the Heavens, arranged for the Purpose of a critical Examination, the Result of which appears to throw some new Light upon the Organization of the celestial Bodies.[a]

Read June 20, 1811.

A KNOWLEDGE of the construction of the heavens has always been the ultimate object of my observations, and having been many years engaged in applying my forty, twenty, and large ten feet telescopes, on account of their great space-penetrating power to review the most interesting objects discovered in my sweeps, as well as those which had before been communicated to the public in the *Connoissance des Temps*, for 1784, I find that by arranging these objects in a certain successive regular order, they may be viewed in a new light, and, if I am not mistaken, an examination of them will lead to consequences which cannot be indifferent to an inquiring mind.

[a] [*Phil. Trans.*, CI (1811), 269–336. This paper and its companion together occupy more than a hundred pages in the original. Fortunately this length is due to Herschel's desire to reduce to a minimum the step from one 'article' to the next and at the same time to multiply his examples, so that the substance of the papers can be reproduced in a shorter space. Thus for some intermediate 'articles' the title alone conveys Herschel's meaning. A bird's eye view of the present paper can be obtained from Herschel's synopsis (below, pp. 147–9).]

If it should be remarked that in this new arrangement I am not entirely consistent with what I have already in former papers said on the nature of some objects that have come under my observation, I must freely confess that by continuing my sweeps of the heavens my opinion of the arrangement of the stars and their magnitudes, and of some other particulars, has undergone a gradual change; and indeed when the novelty of the subject is considered, we cannot be surprised that many things formerly taken for granted, should on examination prove to be different from what they were generally, but incautiously, supposed to be.

For instance, an equal scattering of the stars may be admitted in certain calculations; but when we examine the milky way, or the closely compressed clusters of stars, of which my catalogues have recorded so many instances, this supposed equality of scattering must be given up. We may also have surmised nebulæ to be no other than clusters of stars disguised by their very great distance; but a longer experience and better acquaintance with the nature of nebulæ, will not allow a general admission of such a principle, although undoubtedly a cluster of stars may assume a nebulous appearance when it is too remote for us to discern the stars of which it is composed.[a]

Impressed with an idea that nebulæ properly speaking were clusters of stars, I used to call the nebulosity of which some were composed, when it was of a certain appearance, *resolvable*; but when I perceived that additional light, so far from resolving these nebulæ into stars, seemed to prove that their nebulosity was not different from what I had called milky, this conception was set aside as erroneous. In consequence of this, such nebulæ as afterwards were suspected to consist of stars, or in which a few might be seen, were called *easily resolvable*; but even this expression must be received with caution, because an object may not only contain stars, but also nebulosity not composed of them.

It will be necessary to explain the spirit of the method of arranging the observed astronomical objects under consideration in such a manner, that one shall assist us to understand the nature and construction of the other. This end I propose to obtain by assorting them into as many classes as will be required to produce the most gradual affinity between the individuals contained in any one class with those contained in that which precedes and that which follows it: and it will certainly contribute to the perfection of this method, if this connection between the various classes can be made to appear so clearly as not to admit of a doubt. This consideration will be a sufficient apology for the great number of assortments into which I have

[a] [A frank admission of a valuable assumption abandoned and a major reappraisal undertaken.]

thrown the objects under consideration; and it will be found that those contained in one article, are so closely allied to those in the next, that there is perhaps not so much difference between them, if I may use the comparison, as there would be in an annual description of the human figure, were it given from the birth of a child till he comes to be a man in his prime.

The similarity of the objects contained in each class will seldom require the description of more than one of them, and for this purpose, out of the number referred to, the selected one will be that which has been most circumstantially observed; however, those who wish either to review any other of the objects, or to read a short description of them, will find their place in the heavens, or the account of their appearance either in the catalogues I have given of them in the *Philos. Trans.* or in the *Connoissance des Temps* for 1784, to which in every article proper references will be given for the objects under consideration.

If the description I give should sometimes differ a little from that which belongs to some number referred to, it must be remembered that objects which had been observed many times, could not be so particularly and comprehensively detailed in the confined space of the catalogues as I now may describe them; additional observations have also now and then given me a better view of the objects than I had before. This remark will always apply to the numbers which refer to the *Connoissance des Temps*; for the nebulæ and clusters of stars are there so imperfectly described, that my own observation of them with large instruments may well be supposed to differ entirely from what is said of them. But if any astronomer should review them, with such high space-penetrating-powers, as are absolutely required, it will be found that I have classed them very properly.

It will be necessary to mention that the nebulous delineations in the figures are not intended to represent any of the individuals of the objects which are described otherwise than in the circumstances which are common to the nebulæ of each assortment: the irregularity of a figure, for instance, must stand for every other irregularity; and the delineated size for every other size. It will however be seen, that in the figure referred to there is a sufficient resemblance to the described nebula to show the essential features of shape and brightness then under consideration.

## 1. *Of extensive diffused Nebulosity.*

The first article of my series will begin with extensive diffused nebulosity, which is a phenomenon that hitherto has not been much noticed, and can indeed only be perceived by instruments that collect a great quantity of light. Its existence, when some part of it is pointed out by objects that are within the reach of common telescopes, has nevertheless obtruded itself already on the knowledge of astronomers, as will be seen in my third article.

The widely diffused nebulosity under consideration has already been partially mentioned in my catalogues.[a]

The description of the object I shall select is of No. 14 in the 5th class,[b] and is as follows: "Extremely faint branching nebulosity; its whitishness is entirely of the milky kind, and it is brighter in three or four places than in the rest; the stars of the milky way are scattered over it in the same manner as over the rest of the heavens. Its extent in the parallel is nearly $1\frac{1}{2}$ degree, and in the meridional direction about 52 minutes. The following part of it is divided into several streams and windings, which after separating, meet each other again towards the south." See figure 1 [Plate 6].

This account, which agrees with what will be found in all the other numbers referred to, with regard to the subject under consideration, namely, a diffused milky nebulosity, will give us already some idea of its great abundance in the heavens; my next article however will far extend our conception of its quantity.

2. *Observations of Nebulosities that have not been published before.*[c]

3. *Of Nebulosities joined to Nebulæ.*

4. *Of detached Nebulosities.*

[a] See *Phil. Trans.* 1786, p. 471; 1789, p. 226; and 1802, p. 503. The following ten nebulosities are in the Vth class, No. 13, 14, 15, 17, 28, 30, 31, 33, 34, 38.

[b] [H. V. 14=NGC 6992, the f. part of the Cygnus Loop system. Herschel has previously used this as an example of a "Milky Way" in his 1785 paper (p. 100, note [a]), supposing it to be made of stars: he now regards it, correctly, as true nebulosity.—D.]

[c] [This article 2 is a discussion and list of fifty-two fields "affected with nebulosity". These fields were the subject of considerable controversy in the early decades of this century. See, for example only, P. A. McNally, *Publications of the Astron. Soc. of the Pacific*, XLI (1929), 16: a photographic atlas of the fields has been published (D. Klumpke-Roberts, *Atlas of 52 Regions, A Guide to Herschel's Fields*, Paris, 1929). Many of the fields are in high galactic latitude where little gaseous nebulosity would be expected: some are near the ecliptic and Herschel may have been misled by the zodiacal light. A few do contain patches of nebulosity, but not always answering well to Herschel's description.

Modern photographs with large Schmidt cameras and fast emulsions leave no room for doubt that Herschel was wrong: many of the fields are devoid of any nebulosity of the kind described by Herschel.—D.]

### 5. Of milky Nebulæ.

When detached nebulosities are small we are used to call them nebulæ, and it is already known from my catalogues that their number is very great. . . .[a]

### 6. Of milky Nebulæ with Condensation.

### 7. Of Nebulæ which are brighter in more than one Place.

It is not an uncommon circumstance that the same nebula is brighter in several different places than in the rest of its compass. The following six are of this sort.[b]

No. 213 in the first class[c] is "A very brilliant and considerably large nebula, extended in a direction from south preceding to north following. It seems to have three or four bright nuclei." See fig. 5 [Plate 6].

From this construction of the nebula, we may draw some additional information concerning the point which was left undetermined in my last article; for since there it was proposed as an alternative, that the nebulous matter might either be of a greater depth or more compressed in the brightest part of the nebula then under consideration, we have now an opportunity to examine the probability of each case. If here the appearance of several bright nuclei is to be explained by the depth of the nebulous matter, we must have recourse to three or four separate very slender and deep projections, all situated exactly in the line of sight; but such a very uncommon arrangement of nebulous matter cannot pretend to probability; whereas a moderate condensation, which may indeed be also accompanied with some little general swelling of the nebulous matter about the places which appear like nuclei, will satisfactorily account for their superior brightness.

The same method of reasoning may be as successfully applied to explain the number of unequally bright places in the diffused nebulosities which have been described in the 1st, 2d, and 3d articles. For instance, in the branching nebulosity V. 14,[d] we find three or four places brighter than

[a] [An important definition of terms. ". . . . their number is very great": *most* (but not all) of the nebulæ referred to in this paper we should now call galaxies. Although he discovered and gave catalogue numbers to many gaseous nebulæ in the Milky Way, most of Herschel's new nebulæ are in fact the galaxies in high galactic latitude whose existence in large numbers he was the first to describe.—D.]

[b] See I. 165, 213, 261. II. 297, 406. III. 49.

[c] [H. I. 213 = NGC 4449. A bright galaxy, type Irr I, elongated, with star clouds and patches of emission nebulosity.—D.]

[d] [H. V. 14 = NGC 6992. 'Veil' nebula of Cygnus Loop system.—D.]

WILLIAM HERSCHEL

the rest—in the nebulosity No. 44 of the table[a] we have places of different brightness. In the nebula of Orion, there are many parts that differ much in lustre; and in V. 37[b] of the same article I found, by an observation in the year 1790, the same variety of appearance. In all these cases a proportional condensation of the nebulous matter in the brighter places will sufficiently account for their different degree of shining.

This way of explaining the observed appearances being admitted, it will be proper to enter into an examination of the probable cause of the condensation of the nebulous matter. Should the necessity for such a condensing cause be thought to be admitted upon too slight an induction, a more detailed support of it will hereafter be found in the condition of such a copious collection of objects, as will establish its existence beyond all possibility of doubt.[c]

Instead of inquiring after the nature of the cause of the condensation of nebulous matter, it would indeed be sufficient for the present purpose to call it merely a condensing principle; but since we are already acquainted with the centripetal force of attraction which gives a globular figure to planets, keeps them from flying out of their orbits in tangents, and makes one star revolve around another, why should we not look up to the universal gravitation of matter as the cause of every condensation, accumulation, compression, and concentration of the nebulous matter? Facts are not wanting to prove that such a power has been exerted; and as I shall point out a series of phenomena in the heavens where astronomers may read in legible characters the manifest vestiges of such an exertion, I need not hesitate to proceed in a few additional remarks on the consequences that must arise from the admission of this attractive principle.

The nebula, for instance, which has been described at the beginning of this article, as containing several bright nuclei, has probably so many predominant seats of attraction, arising from a superior preponderance of the nebulous matter in those places; but attraction being a principle which never ceases to act, the consequence of its continual exertion upon this nebula will probably be a division of it, from which will arise three or four

a ["the nebulosity No. 44 of the table": i.e. no. 44 in the table of fifty-two regions given, but not here reproduced, in article 2 above. This area is NGC 7000, the North America nebula.—D.]

b [H. V. 37=NGC 7000, again.

On occasions in this and other papers Herschel seems to have chosen his examples of objects rather hastily from the observing books: differently identified objects from different sweeps are given without Herschel realizing that they are in fact the same object.—D.]

c See Article 24.

138

distinct nebulæ. In the same manner its operation on the diffused nebulosities that have many different bright places, will possibly occasion a breaking up of them into smaller diffusions and detached nebulæ; but before I proceed with conjectures, let us see what observations we have to give countenance to such expectations.

### 8. *Of double Nebulæ with joined Nebulosity.*

### 9. *Of double Nebulæ that are not more than two Minutes from each other.*

To add to the probability of the separation of nebulæ, we ought to have a considerable number of them already separated. The following twenty-three are completely divided although not more than two minutes from one another.[a]

A description of II. 714[b] is "Two pretty bright nebulæ; they are both round, small, and about 2′ from each other, in a meridional direction."

Of III. 755[c] is "Two very faint, very small extended nebulæ within $1\frac{1}{2}′$ from each other."

That all these nebulæ are really double, is founded on the reason already assigned in the last article.[d] Then if we would enter into some kind of examination how they came to be arranged into their binary order, we cannot have recourse to a promiscuous scattering, which by a calculation of chances can never account for such a peculiar distribution of them.[e] If, on the contrary, we look to a division of nebulous matter by the condensing principle, then every parcel of it, which had more than one preponderating seat of attraction in its extent, must in the progress of time have been divided.

No doubt can be suggested on account of the great length of time such a division must have taken up, when we have an eternity of past duration to recur to.

### 10. *Of double Nebulæ at a greater Distance than 2′ from each other.*

[a] See I. 116, 190, 197.   II. 8, 28, 57, 111, 178, 450, 714.   III. 92, 228, 280, 591, 687, 719, 755, 855, 886, 943, 952, 959, 967.

[b] [H. II. 714=NGC 5353. Two close galaxies, E and So, of similar magnitude. —D.]

[c] [H. III. 755=NGC 4403-4. Two close galaxies, E and S, of similar magnitude: the S galaxy show evidence of interaction indicating physical proximity.—D.]

[d] [Most of the twenty-three objects are close pairs of galaxies, some in physical proximity. A few of the nebulæ listed as double nebulæ are in fact relatively large single galaxies in which Herschel has seen two brighter separate condensations of light and listed them as separate objects in his catalogue. Different parts of a single large galaxy may bear different NGC numbers for this reason.—D.]

[e] [Herschel gladly adapts the earlier probability arguments in favour of binary systems of stars, above, pp. 36 seq.]

## 11. *Of treble, quadruple, and sextuple Nebulæ.*[a]

## 12. *Of the remarkable Situation of Nebulæ.*

The number of compound[b] nebulæ that have been noticed in the foregoing three articles being so considerable, it will follow, that if they owe their origin to the breaking up of some former extensive nebulosities of the same nature with those which have been shewn to exist at present, we might expect that the number of separate nebulæ should far exceed the former, and that moreover these scattered nebulæ should be found not only in great abundance, but also in proximity or continuity with each other, according to the different extents and situations of the former diffusions of such nebulous matter. Now this is exactly what by observation, we find to be the state of the heavens.

In the following seven assortments we have not less than 424 nebulæ; some of them of unascertained size, figure, or condensation; and the rest with only the first of these three essential features recorded.

The reason for not having a more circumstantial account of such a number of objects, is that they crowded upon me at the time of sweeping in such quick succession, that of sixty-one I could but just secure the place in the heavens, and of the remaining three hundred and sixty-three, I had only time to add the relative size.[c]

[a] [Herschel lists twenty examples and describes three in detail. They are mostly closely-grouped galaxies. The first described is however H. V. 10=NGC 6514, the 'Trifid' nebula (gaseous). The other two are H. III. 358=NGC 4169, 73, 74, 75, four galaxies in a close group; and H. III. 391=NGC 4070, . . . six galaxies, the brightest at the N.f. end of a scattered cluster.]

[b] ["The number of compound nebulæ . . . noticed in the foregoing three articles". Compound here apparently used in the sense of double, triple or multiple, rather than in the sense (compound nebula=a Milky Way) of p. 89. Although a few gaseous nebulæ like NGC 6514 (the 'Trifid') have been included, most of the nebulæ referred to are close pairs or groups of galaxies.

The substance of this article 12 is to draw attention to large numbers of nebulæ, almost all galaxies, and remark upon their concentration in certain areas of sky, especially in the constellations of Virgo, Coma, etc., with subsidiary concentrations in three areas ("branches") in Bootes, Ursa Major, and Leo. The areas where "the absence of nebulæ is as remarkable . . . " are for the greater part in lower galactic latitude or free from prominent groupings of galaxies like those near the north galactic pole.—D.]

[c] See *sixty-one nebulæ . . . Ten extremely small nebulæ . . . One hundred and thirty six very small nebulæ . . . Forty-two not very small nebulæ . . . One hundred and seven small nebulæ . . . Fifty-eight pretty large nebulæ . . . Ten large nebulæ . . .* [Catalogue numbers not reproduced.]

Neither of the nebulæ in these seven divisions will require a description, as the title of each assortment contains all that has been ascertained about them; but their number and situation, especially when added to those that will be contained in the following articles, completely supports what has been asserted, namely, that the present state of the heavens presents us with several extensive collections of scattered nebulæ, plainly indicating by their very remarkable arrangement, that they owe their origin to some former common stock of nebulous matter.

To refer astronomers to the heavens for an inspection of these and the following nebulæ, would be to propose a repetition of more than eleven hundred sweeps to them, but those who wish to have some idea of the nebulous arrangements may consult MR. BODE'S excellent *Atlas Cœlestis*. A succession of places where the nebulæ of my catalogues are uncommonly crowded, will there be seen beginning over the tail of Hydra and proceeding to the southern wing, the body and the northern wing of Virgo, Plate 14. Then to Coma Berenices, Canes venatici, and the preceding arm of Bootes, Plate 7. A different branch goes from Coma Berenices to the hind legs of Ursa major. Another branch passes from the wing of Virgo to the tail and body of Leo, Plate 8.

It will not be necessary to point out many other smaller collections which may be found in several plates of the same Atlas.

On the other hand, a very different aspect of the heavens will be perceived when we examine the following constellations. Beginning from the head of Capricorn, Plate 16, thence proceeding to Antinous, to the tail of Aquila, Plate 9, to Ramus Cerberus, and the body of Hercules, Plate 8, to Quadrans Muralis, Plate 7, and to the head of Draco, Plate 3. We may also examine the constellations of Auriga, Lynx, and Camelopardalus, Plate 5.

In this second review, it will be found that here the absence of nebulæ is as remarkable, as the great multitude of them in the first mentioned series of constellations.

13. *Of very narrow long Nebulæ.*

14. *Of extended Nebulæ.*

15. *Of Nebulæ that are of an irregular Figure.*

16. *Of Nebulæ that are of an irregular round Figure.*

17. *Of round Nebulæ.*

18. *Of Nebulæ that are remarkable for some particularity in Figure or Brightness.*

### 19. *Of Nebulæ that are gradually a little brighter in the middle.*[a]

The investigation of the form of the nebulous matter in the 13, 14, 15, and 16th articles has been founded only upon the observed figure of nebulæ; and in the 17th article the globular form of this matter deduced from the round appearance of nebulæ, has been ascribed to the action of the gravitating principle. I am now entering upon an examination of nebulæ of which, besides their figure, I have also recorded the different degrees of light, and the situation of the greatest brightness with respect to their figure. These observations will establish the former conclusions by an additional number of objects, and by the decisive argument of their brightness, which points out a seat of attraction.

In the following four assortments are one hundred and fifty nebulæ, which all agree in being a little brighter in the middle. This increase of brightness must be understood to be always very gradual from the outside towards the middle of the nebula, whatever be its figure; and although this circumstance, for want of time, has often been left unnoticed in the observation, I am very sure that had the gradation of brightness been otherwise, it would certainly not have been overlooked.[b]

III. 853 is "A very faint small nebula; it is very gradually a little brighter in the middle."

III. 488 is "A very faint extended nebula, near 3' long, and above 2' broad; it is gradually a little brighter in the middle." Fig. 13 [Plate 6].

II. 549 is "A very large and pretty bright nebula of an irregular figure; it is a little brighter in the middle." Fig. 14 [Plate 6].

II. 812 is "A faint, small, round nebula; it is very gradually a little brighter in the middle, and the increase of brightness begins at a distance from the center." Fig. 15 [Plate 6].

It is hardly necessary to say that the united testimony of so many objects can leave no doubt about the central seat of attraction, which in every instance of figure is pointed out to be in the middle.

The only remark I have to make, relates to the exertion of the condensing power, which in the case of these nebulæ appears to have produced but a very moderate effect. This may be ascribed either to the unshapen

a [The nebulæ referred to in articles 13–19, several hundred in number, have not been examined individually; but the type objects described in detail are all galaxies.—D.]

b See *thirty-two nebulæ, the particular figure of which has not been ascertained, gradually a little brighter in the middle.* . . . *Twenty-four extended nebulæ, gradually a little brighter in the middle.* . . . *Twenty nebulæ of an irregular figure, gradually a little brighter in the middle.* . . . *Seventy-four round or nearly round nebulæ, gradually a little brighter in the middle.* . . . [Catalogue numbers not reproduced.]

mass of nebulous matter which would require much time before it could come to some central arrangement of form either in length, or in length and breadth, or lastly in all its three dimensions. It may also be ascribed to the small quantity of the preponderating central attractive matter; or even to the shortness of its time of acting: for in this case millions of years, perhaps are but moments.

### 20. Of Nebulæ which are gradually brighter in the middle.

By the general description of a nebula, when it is said to be gradually brighter in the middle, we are to understand that its light was observed to be obviously brighter about the center than in other parts. Had the nebulæ of this class been only a little brighter, or had they been much brighter in the middle, such additional expressions would certainly have been used; except where time would not allow to be more particular. I have sorted two hundred and twenty-three of these nebulæ like the foregoing, according to their figure, into four classes.[a]

II. 409[b] is "A pretty bright and pretty large nebula; it is very gradually brighter in the middle."

I. 55[c] is "A considerably bright, extended nebula about 4' long and 2' broad, in a meridional direction; it is gradually brighter in the middle." Fig. 16 [Plate 6].

I. 266[d] is "A considerably bright, and pretty large nebula, of an irregular figure; it is gradually brighter in the middle." Fig. 17 [Plate 6].

I. 98[e] is "A considerably bright, and pretty large round nebula; it is brighter in the middle, the brightness diminishing very gradually from the center towards the circumference." Fig. 18 [Plate 6].

From the account of these nebulæ, we find again that all what has been said concerning the seat of the forming and condensing power of the nebulous matter, is abundantly confirmed by observation.

I have only to remark that, the exertion of the gravitating principle in these nebulæ, is in a more advanced state than with those of the last article; and that the same conceptions which have already been suggested, namely,

[a] See *Thirty-nine nebulæ of an unascertained figure, gradually brighter in the middle.* . . . *Fifty extended nebulæ gradually brighter in the middle.* . . . *Twenty-nine nebulæ of an irregular figure, gradually brighter in the middle.* . . . *One hundred and five round, or nearly round nebulæ, gradually brighter in the middle.* . . . [Catalogue numbers not reproduced.]

[b] [H. II. 409=NGC 4190, galaxy—D.]

[c] [H. I. 55=NGCb 7479, SBb galaxy—D.]

[d] [H. I. 266=NGC 3206, S galaxy—D.]

[e] [H. I. 98=NGC 5273, So galaxy—D.]

the original form of the nebulous matter; its quantity in the seat of the attracting principle; and the length of the time of its action, when properly considered, will sufficiently account for the present state of these nebulæ.

21. *Of Nebulæ that are gradually much brighter in the middle.*

22. *Of Nebulæ that have a Cometic appearance.*

Among the numerous nebulæ I have seen, there are many that have the appearance of telescopic comets. The following are of that sort.[a]

I. 4[b] is "A pretty large cometic nebula of considerable brightness; it is much brighter in the middle, and the very faint chevelure is pretty extensive." Fig. 22 [Plate 6].

By the appellation of cometic, it was my intention to express a gradual and strong increase of brightness towards the center of a nebulous object of a round figure; having also a faint chevelure or coma of some extent, beyond the faintest part of the light, gradually decreasing from the center.

It seems that this species of nebulæ contains a somewhat greater degree of condensation than that of the round nebulæ of the last article, and might perhaps not very improperly have been included in their number. Their great resemblance to telescopic comets, however, is very apt to suggest the idea, that possibly such small telescopic comets as often visit our neighbourhood may be composed of nebulous matter, or may in fact be such highly condensed nebulæ.

23. *Of Nebulæ that are suddenly much brighter in the middle.*

24. *Of round Nebulæ increasing gradually in brightness up to a Nucleus in the middle.*

25. *Of Nebulæ that have a Nucleus.*

26. *Of extended Nebulæ that shew the Progress of Condensation.*

When the nebulous matter is much extended in length, it appears from the following nebulæ, that with those which have a nucleus completely formed, the nebulosity on each side of it is comparatively reduced to a fainter state than it is in nebulæ of which the nucleus is apparently still in an incipient state. These faint opposite appendages to the nucleus I have in my observations called branches.

In some nebulæ there is also an additional small faint nebulosity of a

[a] See *Seventeen cometic nebulæ.* I. 3, 4, 34, 217.   II. 6, 15, 33, 59, 104, 153, 154, 241, 315, 404.   III. 5, 21. *Connoiss.* 95.

[b] [H. I. 4=NGC 3169, an Sa galaxy—D.]

circular form about the nucleus, and this I have called the chevelure. The following two assortments contain twenty-eight nebulæ of this kind.[a]

Number 65 of the *Connoissance*[b] is "A very brilliant nebula extended in the meridian, about 12' long. It has a bright nucleus, the light of which suddenly diminishes on its border, and two opposite very faint branches." Fig. 29 [Plate 7].

I. 205[c] is "A very brilliant nebula, 5' or 6' long and 3 or 4' broad; it has a small bright nucleus with a faint chevelure about it, and two opposite very extensive branches." Fig. 30 [Plate 7].

The construction of these nebulæ is certainly complicated and mysterious, and in our present state of knowledge it would be presumptuous to attempt an explanation of it; we can only form a few distant surmises, which however may lead to the following queries.[d] May not the faintness of the branches arise from a gradual diminution, of the length and density of the nebulous matter contained in them, occasioned by its gravitation towards the nucleus into which it probably subsides? Are not these faint nebulous branches joining to a nucleus, upon an immense scale, somewhat like what the zodiacal light is to our sun in miniature? Does not the chevelure denote that perhaps some of the nebulous matter still remaining in the branches, before it subsides into the nucleus, begins to take a spherical form, and thus assumes the semblance of a faint chevelure surrounding it in a concentric arrangement? And, if we may venture to extend these queries a little farther—will not the matter of these branches in their gradual fall towards the nucleus, when discharging their substance into the chevelure, produce a kind of vortex or rotatory motion? Must not such an effect take place, unless we suppose, contrary to observation, that one branch is exactly like the other; that both are exactly in a line passing through the center of the nucleus, by way of causing exactly an equal stream of it from each branch to enter the chevelure at opposite sides; and, this not being probable, do we not see some natural cause which may give a rotatory motion to a celestial body in its very formation?

[a] See *Twenty-three extended nebulæ with a nucleus and two opposite faint branches.* I. 9, 13, 15, 27, 32, 75, 130, 160, 163, 187, 188, 195, 223, 228, 230. II. 101, 650, 733. IV. 61. V. 43. *Connoiss.* 65, 83, 98.

*Five with a nucleus, chevelure and branches.* I. 194, 205, 210. V. 45. *Connoiss.* 94.

[b] [M65 = NGC 3623, a bright Sc galaxy seen steeply inclined, though not edge-on.—D.]

[c] [H. I. 205 = NGC 2841, an inclined Sb galaxy with a very bright nucleus and lens-shaped inner region.—D.]

[d] [These rhetorical queries are surely a conscious stylistic echo of the queries to Newton's *Opticks*.]

27. *Of round Nebulæ that shew the Progression of Condensation.*

28. *Of round Nebulæ that are of an almost uniform Light.*

29. *Of Nebulæ that draw progressively towards a Period of final Condensation.*

In the course of the gradual condensation of the nebulous matter, it may be expected that a time must come when it can no longer be compressed, and the only cause which we may suppose to put an end to the compression is, when the consolidated matter assumes hardness. It remains therefore to be examined, how far my observations will go to ascertain the intensity of its consolidation.

The following two assortments contain seven nebulæ, from whose appearance a considerable degree of solidity may be inferred.[a]

IV. 55[b] is "A pretty bright round nebula, almost of an even light throughout approaching to a planetary appearance, but ill defined, and a little fainter on the edges; it is about ¾ or 1 minute in diameter." Fig. 34.[c]

IV. 37[d] is "A very bright planetary disk of about 35″ in diameter, but ill defined on the edges; the center of it is rather more luminous than the rest, and with long attention a very bright well defined round center becomes visible." Fig. 35 [Plate 7].

In these nebulæ we have three different indications of the compression of the nebulous matter of which they are composed: their figure, their light, and the small compass into which it is reduced. The round figure is a proof that the nebulous mass is collected into a globular form, which cannot have been effected without a certain degree of condensation. . . .

30. *Of Planetary Nebulæ.*

31. *Of the Distance of the Nebula in the Constellation of Orion.*

32. *Of Stellar Nebulæ.*

33. *Of Stellar Nebulæ nearly approaching to the Appearance of Stars.*

34. *Of doubtful Nebulæ.*

35. *Concluding Remarks.*

The total dissimilitude between the appearance of a diffusion of the nebulous matter and of a star, is so striking, that an idea of the conversion

[a] See *Four nebulæ of a planetary appearance.* IV. 55, 60, 68, 78. *Three planetary disks with a bright central point.* II. 268. IV. 37, 73.
[b] [H. IV. 55=NGC 2537, Sc galaxy.—D.]  [c] [Plate 7.]
[d] [H. IV. 37=NGC 6543, planetary nebula.—D.]

of the one into the other can hardly occur to any one who has not before him the result of the critical examination of the nebulous system which has been displayed in this paper. The end I have had in view, by arranging my observations in the order in which they have been placed, has been to shew, that the above mentioned extremes may be connected by such nearly allied intermediate steps, as will make it highly probable that every succeeding state of the nebulous matter is the result of the action of gravitation upon it while in a foregoing one, and by such steps the successive condensation of it has been brought up to the planetary condition. From this the transit to the stellar form, it has been shown, requires but a very small additional compression of the nebulous matter, and several instances have been given which connect the planetary to the stellar appearance.

The faint stellar nebulæ have also been well connected with all sorts of faint nebulæ of a larger size; and in a number of the smaller sort, their approach to the starry appearance is so advanced, that in my observations of many of them it became doubtful whether they were not stars already.

It must have been noticed, that I have confined myself in every one of the preceding articles to a few remarks upon the appearance of the nebulous matter in the state in which my observations represented it; they seemed to be the natural result of the observations under consideration, and were not given with a view to establish a systematic opinion, such as will admit of complete demonstration. The observations themselves are arranged so conveniently that any astronomer, chemist, or philosopher, after having considered my critical remarks, may form what judgment appears most probable to him. At all events, the subject is of such a nature as cannot fail to attract the notice of every inquisitive mind to a contemplation of the stupendous construction of the heavens; and what I have said may at least serve to throw some new light upon the organization of the celestial bodies.

### Synopsis of the Contents of this Paper

## POSTSCRIPT.

IT will be seen that in this paper I have only considered the nebulous part of the construction of the heavens, and have taken a star for the limit of my researches. The rich collection of clusters of stars contained in the 6th, 7th, and 8th classes of my Catalogues, and many of the *Connoissance des Temps*, have as yet been left unnoticed. Several other objects, in which stars and nebulosity are mixed, such as nebulous stars, nebulæ containing stars, or suspected clusters of stars which yet may be nebulæ, have not been introduced, as they appeared to belong to the sidereal part of the construction of the heavens, into a critical examination of which it was not my intention to enter in this Paper.

WILLIAM HERSCHEL.

Slough, near Windsor,
May 26, 1811.

[In the preceding thirty-three 'articles', in which Herschel arranges examples of nebulæ principally to show the probability of condensation from "extensive diffused Nebulosity" to "Stellar Nebulæ nearly approaching to the Appearance of Stars", he cites altogether several hundred examples of nebulæ. It would be a major task to identify their NGC numbers and their nature. But from the type objects that Herschel describes in a little more detail, it is clear that *most* of the objects that he is talking about in the later articles (after article 5) are not gaseous objects at all, but galaxies! There is, however, an occasional bright and compact galactic nebulosity (e.g. the "Trifid" in article 11) and of course article 30 relates to planetary nebulæ. A few other objects in the later articles on "condensed nebulæ" are also planetary nebulæ.

It might seem strange that Herschel should see so many galaxies as essentially star-like objects or "very much brighter towards the middle", with a faint halo or "chevelure" about the bright nucleus. It must be remembered that Herschel was seeing only the brighter central regions of galaxies, not the faint outer parts and spiral arms recorded on modern photographs. Now the familiar textbook reproductions of galaxies are very misleading in suggesting a more or less uniformly bright central area from which (in spirals) the arms emerge. On visual inspection, or good original negatives of short exposure, many galaxies (perhaps most) show a rapid increase in brightness to an astonishingly small and bright central nucleus of almost stellar dimensions. This feature is almost always lost in photographic reproduction, and is one with which many modern astronomers who have not worked on galaxies are unfamiliar.

In this paper of 1811 Herschel is further from the truth (in that he supposes galaxies to be of a gaseous nature and condensing) than he was in 1789, when he thought that most small nebulous objects were made of unresolved stars. But although his interpretation is incorrect, the observations are perfectly sound, and Herschel may fairly be said to have been the first person to discover (as we should now say) that many galaxies have a bright star-like nucleus.—D.]

# Astronomical Observations relating to the sidereal part of the Heavens, and its Connection with the nebulous part: arranged for the purpose of a critical Examination.[a]

Read February 24, 1814.

IN my paper of observations of the nebulous part of the heavens, I have endeavoured to shew the probability of a very gradual conversion of the nebulous matter into the sidereal appearance. The observations contained in this paper are intended to display the sidereal part of the heavens, and

[a] [*Phil. Trans.*, CIV (1814), 248–84.]

also to shew the intimate connection between the two opposite extremes, one of which is the immensity of the widely diffused and seemingly chaotic nebulous matter; and the other, the highly complicated and most artificially constructed globular clusters of compressed stars.

The proof of an intimate connection between these extremes will greatly support the probability of the conversion of the one into the other; and in order to make this connection gradually visible, I have arranged my observations into a series of collections, such as I suppose will best answer the end of a critical examination.

1. *Of Stars in remarkable situations with regard to Nebulæ.*[a]

2. *Of two Stars with nebulosity between them.*[b]

A more remarkable situation than the former is that of two stars with nebulosity between them, or both included in the same nebulosity.

III. 67[c] is "An extremely faint nebulosity extended from one star to a smaller one, at the distance of about 2 minutes south of the former." See fig. 2 [Plate 8].

II. 706.[d] "Two considerable stars are involved in a very faint nebulosity of 3 or 4 minutes in extent." See fig. 3 [Plate 8].

Here I have referred to 19 instances, where two stars have an extended nebulosity between them, or at least are both contained within it. Now, if we were to enter into a calculation of chances to investigate the probability that in every one of these 19 objects, the stars and the nebulosity should be unconnected, we should have to consider that in order to produce this appearance by three objects at a distance from each other, it would be required that every one of them should be precisely in a given line of sight, and that the nebulosity should not only be in the middle of them, but that it also should be extended from the situation of one star to that of the other; and that all this should happen in the confined space of a few minutes of a degree; which cannot be probable. Then, if on the other hand we recollect that in the 8th, 9th, and 10th articles of my paper on the nebulous part of the heavens, I have given 139 double nebulæ joined by nebulosity between them, and that we have now before us 19 similar objects, with no other difference than that instead of nebulæ we have stars

a [These are galaxies close to foreground stars.—D.]

b See nineteen double stars joined by intermediate nebulosity II. 16, 706, 732. III. 19, 32, 67, 68, 113, 126, 182, 200, 312, 376, 540, 637, 757, 785, 820, 854.

c [H. III. 67=NGC 3473, S galaxy between two foreground stars.—D.]

d [H. II. 706=NGC 7538, a small compact gaseous (galactic) nebulosity with two stars involved.—D.]

with nebulosity remaining between them, should we not surmise that possibly these stars had formerly been highly condensed nebulæ, like those that have been mentioned, and were now by gradually increasing condensation turned into small stars; and may not the nebulosity still remaining shew their nebulous origin?

When to this is added that we also have an account of 700 double stars entirely free from nebulosity,[a] many of which are probably at no great real distance from each other, it seems as if we had these double objects in three different successive conditions: first as nebulæ; next as stars with remaining nebulosity; and lastly as stars completely free from nebulous appearance.

### 3. *Of Stars with nebulosities of various shapes attached to them.*

When a nebula seems to be joined to a star, or closely pointing to it, the manner of its appearance deserves our attention. Here follow three different sorts of such conjunctions.[b]

First sort; I. 143.[c] "On the north preceding side of a pretty bright star is a considerable, bright nebulosity. It is joined to the star so as to appear like a brush to it." See fig. 4 [Plate 8].

Second sort; IV. 4.[d] "A very small star has an extremely faint, and very small nebula attached to it in the shape of a puff." See fig. 5 [Plate 8].

Third sort; IV. 35.[e] "A small star has a small, faint, fan-shaped nebulosity joining to it on the north preceding side." See fig. 6 [Plate 8].

Here we have a list of fourteen objects,[f] in which the probability of a union between the nebulosities and the stars will gradually become more apparent. With regard to the first nine, the particularity of their construction is already very pointed: the conditions are that the nebulosity must be extended; the direction of its extension must be exactly towards the star,

[a] See *Phil. Trans.* for 1782, page 112; and for 1785, page 40.
[b] See fourteen stars connected with nebulæ.
Nine with a brush I. 143.    II. 214, 683.    III. 643.    IV. 10, 17, 29, 40, 77.
Two with a puff IV. 3, 4.
Three with fan-shaped nebulosity IV. 2, 35, 66.
[c] [H. I. 143=NGC 4900, Sc galaxy near star.—D.]
[d] [H. IV. 4=NGC 3662, galaxy and foreground star.—D.]
[e] [H. IV. 35=NGC 2610, planetary nebula and near-by star.—D.]
[f] [The fourteen examples listed are of objects of various physical natures. Most are galaxies with fortuitous foreground stars near by, but a few are stars in the vicinity of gaseous or reflection nebulosity. One is, in the modern sense, "a star with nebulosity attached": H. IV. 2=NGC 2261, Hubble's variable nebula with the variable star R Monocerotis at its tip.—D.]

and it must also be apparently just near enough to touch it; but that all this should happen cannot be probable; whereas a real contact of the objects, held together by mutual gravitation, will readily account for the whole appearance.

In the two next objects there is already some indication of a union between the nebula and the star, for the roundness of the nebulosity appeared to be a little drawn out of its figure towards the star.

But the last three instances, in which the whole mass of nebulous matter is pointedly directed to the stars, and in contact with them, can hardly leave any room for doubting a union between them.

Now if we admit a contact, or union between these nebulæ and the stars, it deserves to be remarked that stars, in the situation of these fourteen, cannot have been formed from their adjoining nebulosities; for a gradual condensation of the nebulous matter would have been central; whereas the stars are at the extremity of the nebulæ. It is therefore reasonable to suppose that their conjunction must be owing to some motion either of the stars or of the nebulous matter: a mutual attraction might draw them together. In either of these cases it would follow, that if the nebulosity should subside into the star, as seems to be indicated by the assumed form of the fan-shaped nebulæ, the star would receive an increase of matter proportional to the magnitude and density of the nebulosity in contact with it. This would give us the idea of what might be called the *growth* of stars.

### 4. *Of Stars with nebulous branches.*

That an intimate connection between the nebulous matter and a star is not incompatible with their nature will clearly appear by the following instances, in which a union is manifested that cannot be mistaken for a deceptive appearance.[a]

IV. 42[b] is "A star of about the 8th or 9th magnitude with very faint nebulous branches extended in the direction of the meridian: each branch is about one minute in length. Other stars of the same size, and at the same time in view, are free from these branches." See fig. 7 [Plate 8].

The three objects to which I have referred shew sufficiently that stars and nebulæ may be connected; for a little swelling and increase of light of the branches, at their junction with the star, which generally takes place, seems evidently to be an effect arising from the gravitation of the nebulous matter towards a center, in which the star is situated.

Here again the visible effect of gravitation supports the idea of the

[a] See three stars with nebulous branches IV. 42, 43, 48.
[b] [H. IV. 42=NGC 676, star and E6 galaxy.—D.]

*growth* of stars by the gradual access of nebulous matter; for in the present case I may refer to the observations already published in the *Phil. Trans.* for 1811, where, page 301,[a] we have an account of twenty-four extended nebulæ, gradually a little brighter in the middle; page 303 there are fifty extended nebulæ, with an increased brightness towards the middle;[b] page 304, we have fifty-four extended nebulæ, with a much greater accumulation of brightness; page 307 there are seven extended nebulæ, in which the central increase of brightness approaches towards the formation of a nucleus. Page 309, we have twenty-seven extended nebulæ, in which the central nucleus is already formed; and finally, page 311 contains the account of twenty-three extended nebulæ, where the nebulosity seems to have so far subsided into the nucleus, as to leave only two opposite faint branches.[c] Who then that has followed up the gradual condensation of an extended nebula till it appeared in the shape of a bright nucleus with faint branches, and finds now in the center of two such opposite faint branches, instead of a condensed nucleus, a star—who, I may ask, would not rather admit that the nucleus had gradually cleared up in brightness, and assumed the lustre of a star, than have recourse to the most improbable of all hypotheses, that a fortuitous central meeting of a star and a nebula should be the cause of such a singular appearance?

### 5. *Of nebulous Stars.*[d]

### 6. *Of Stars connected with extensive windings of nebulosity.*[e]

### 7. *Of small patches consisting of Stars mixed with nebulosity.*

When a small patch of stars is mixed with nebulosity, there is a possibility of its being a deception arising from their being accidentally in the same line of sight; but it has already been shewn that in such appearances the probability is much in favour of a real union; especially when the objects are numerous;[f] and in that case there are but two ways of accounting for it.

[a] [Above, p. 142.]     [b] [Above, p. 143.]     [c] [Above, p. 145.]

[d] See thirteen nebulous stars IV. 19, 25, 36, 38, 44, 45, 52, 57, 58, 65, 69, 71, 74. [These objects are mostly planetary nebulæ, with a few stars involved in diffuse galactic nebulosity.—D.]

[e] See three stars connected with diffusions of nebulosity IV. 24, 33. V. 27. [Stars involved in diffuse galactic nebulosity, including H. V. 27=NGC 2264, the star cluster and complex of gaseous and obscuring matter around 15 Monocerotis.—D.]

[f] See thirty-seven small patches, consisting of stars mixed with nebulosity. [Catalogue numbers not reproduced.]

First, admitting from what has been said, that stars may be formed of nebulous matter, it may happen that the nebulosity still mixed with them is some remaining unsubsided part of that from which they were formed; and in the next place, a union of stars and nebulosity, originally at a distance from each other, may have been effected by the motion of either the stars or the nebulosity.

That such motions may happen has been shewn in the third article, which contains instances of the conjunction of stars with nebulosities of which they cannot have been formed, and which must, consequently, have been united by motion. We also know that nebulæ are subject to great changes in their appearance, which proves that some of the nebulous matter in their composition must be in motion; instances of which have been given in the luminous nebulosity of the constellation of Orion.[a] It may therefore be easily conceived that any moving patch of nebulous matter must be arrested on its meeting with stars; especially if several of them should happen to be pretty near each other; in which case there will be, as it were, a net spread out for intercepting every nebulosity that comes within the reach of their attraction.

II. 304.[b] "Three or four stars of various sizes are mixed with pretty strong nebulosity."

III. 165.[c] "Five or six stars forming a parallelogram, are mixed with very faint milky nebulosity."

III. 697.[d] "Several small stars are contained in faint nebulosity about 3 or 4 minutes long and ¾ broad." See fig. 10 [Plate 8].

IV. 75.[e] "Three stars of about the 9th or 10th magnitude are involved in pretty strong milky nebulosity."

This collection of thirty-seven objects, consisting of 2, 3, 4, 5, 6, or more small stars that are mixed with nebulosity, contains a variety of instances in which the effect that has been mentioned of the interception of the nebulous matter may have taken place. It is very obvious that nothing positive can be said about the formation of so many starry-nebulous patches; for unless by long continued observation of the same patches we could be acquainted with every change that may happen in the nebulosity or in the magnitude of the stars which apparently compose

[a] *Phil. Trans.* for 1811, p. 320. [Compare, above p. 117.]

[b] [H. II. 304=NGC 2316, star in small patch of reflection nebulosity.—D.]

[c] [H. III. 165=NGC 7186, Herschel's object is not identifiable; the area he gives has numerous faint stars around, but no nebulosity.—D.]

[d] [H. III. 697=NGC 4183, a narrow, much elongated galaxy, probably an Irr type seen edge-on, superposed stars and some bright condensations.—D.]

[e] [H. IV. 75=NGC 7129, three stars in bright reflection nebulosity.—D.]

them, their real union and construction must remain unknown. We can only hint, that every nebulosity which is carried into the region of a small patch of stars will probably be gradually arrested and absorbed by them, and that thus the *growth of stars* may be continued.

### 8. *Of objects of an ambiguous construction.*

From objects consisting decidedly of stars, but which either have nebulosity mixed with them, or are in such situations as to be seen in the same line with nebulosity, I proceed to give an account of some others, of which my observations have not ascertained into what order we ought to class them.

It has been remarked, on a former occasion, that clusters of stars, when they are at a great distance, may assume a nebulous appearance.[a] This may be experienced by observing a certain celestial object with a telescope of an inferior space-penetrating power, through which it will be seen as a nebula; whereas with an instrument which has a higher degree of this power, its appearance will be a mixture of nebulosity and stars; and if this power of the telescope is of a still higher order, the stars of the same object will then be distinctly perceived: the nebulosity will no longer be seen, and the object will be entitled to be placed into the rank of clusters of stars.

Other objects there are, where a greater space-penetrating power will only increase the brightness of the nebulosity, and at the same time make the tinge of it more uniformly united and of a milky appearance, which will decide it to be purely nebulous.

But when an object is of such a construction, or at such a distance from us, that the highest power of penetration, which hitherto has been applied to it, leaves it undetermined whether it belong to the class of nebulæ or of stars, it may then be called ambiguous. As there is, however, a considerable difference in the ambiguity of such objects, I have arranged 71 of them into the following four collections.[b]

The first contains seven objects that may be supposed to consist of stars, but where the observations hitherto made, of either their appearance or form, leave it undecided into which class they should be placed.

*Connoiss.* 31[c] is "A large nucleus with very extensive nebulous branches, but the nucleus is very gradually joined to them. The stars which are

[a] *Phil. Trans.* for 1811, page 270. [Above, p. 134.]

[b] See seventy-one ambiguous objects, in four collections. [Catalogue numbers not reproduced.]

[c] [M31=NGC 224, the Andromeda galaxy. In 1795 he gave it as an example of a "Milky Way": now, although it is "supposed to consist of stars" he regards its nature as "ambiguous".–D.]

scattered over it appear to be behind it, and seem to lose part of their lustre in the passage of their light through the nebulosity; there are not more of them scattered over the nebula than there are over the immediate neighbourhood. I examined it in the meridian with a mirror 24 inches in diameter, and saw it in high perfection; but its nature remains mysterious. Its light, instead of appearing resolvable with this aperture, seemed to be more milky."

The objects in this collection must at present remain ambiguous.

The next contains 26 nebulous objects, of which the figure has been ascertained to be round or nearly round.

II. 101ᵃ is "A pretty large, round, extremely faint, easily resolvable nebula. I can almost see the stars in it." See fig 11 [Plate 8].

*Connoiss.* 57ᵇ is "An oval nebula with an eccentric oval dark space in the middle; there is a strong suspicion of its consisting of stars. The diameter, measured by the large 10 feet telescope, is 1′ 28″·3."

The globular form of the objects in this collection, which is deduced from their round figure, will so far ascertain the manner of their construction, that they must either be still in a condensed state purely nebulous, or else, if consisting of stars, that they must be already in a far advanced order of compression, and only appear nebulous on account of their very great distance from us. A middle state between the progressive condensation of a globular nebula and a cluster of stars can have no existence; because a globular nebulosity when condensed can only produce a single star. There is, however, a possibility that a mass of nebulous matter in motion may be intercepted by a globular cluster, in which case the nebulosity must soon assume the form of the cluster, and will finally be absorbed by it.

In the third collection I have placed 26 nebulæ, which not only are described as easily resolvable, but in most of which some stars have actually been seen.

II. 500ᶜ is "A very large, easily resolvable, extended, nebulous object. I see a few of the largest stars in it." See fig. 12 [Plate 8].

Here the uncertainty in which the descriptions leave us, is that the objects in this collection may be either clusters of stars mixed with nebulosity, or that in consequence of the great distance and compression of the small stars composing a cluster which contains no nebulosity, it may put on the nebulous appearance.

ᵃ [H. II. 101=NGC 3489, bright galaxy, So pec. Note Herschel's use of the word resolvable—"easily resolvable. . . . I can almost see the stars in it." The stars were far beyond his reach.—D.]

ᵇ [M57=NGC 6720, planetary, the ring nebula in Lyra.—D.]

ᶜ [H. II. 500=NGC 4535, Sc galaxy.—D.]

The fourth collection contains 12 nebulous objects, of which the description makes it probable that they belong to the order of clusters of stars.

I. 249[a] is "A considerably bright extended nebula about 4' long and 2' broad; it is easily resolvable, and I suppose with a higher power and longer attention the stars would become visible. It is brighter about the middle."

*Connoiss.* 100 is[b] "A nebula of about 10' in diameter, but there is in the middle of it, a small, bright cluster of supposed stars."

### 9. *Of the sidereal part of the Heavens.*

The foregoing observations have proved the intimate connection between the nebulous and sidereal condition; and although in passing from one to the other we have met with a number of ambiguous objects, it has been seen that the apparent uncertainty of their construction is only the consequence of the want of an adequate power in our telescopes, to shew them of their real form. We have indeed no reason to expect that an increase of light and distinctness of our telescopes would free us from ambiguous objects; for by improving our power of penetrating into space, and resolving those which we have at present, we should probably reach so many new objects that others, of an equally obscure construction, would obtrude themselves, even in greater number, on account of the increased space of the more distant regions of their situation.

From stars mixed with nebulosity we are now to direct our attention to the purely sidereal part of the heavens; and as stars are the elementary parts of sidereal constructions, it will be proper to review what we know of their nature. Having already entered upon this subject in a former paper at some length,[c] I shall only give a few additional observations, with a summary outline of the former arguments.

The intensity of the light of a star of the first magnitude may be compared with solar light, by considering, that if the sun were removed to the distance at which we generally admit the brightest stars to be from us, its visible diameter could not exceed the 215th part of a second; and its appearance therefore would probably not differ much from the size and brightness of such stars. By reversing this argument we shall be authorised to conclude, from analogy, that stars, were they near enough, would

[a] [H. I. 249=NGC 2742, Sc galaxy.—D.]

[b] [M100=NGC 4321, bright Sc galaxy. It seems possible that Herschel saw some of the bright condensations that constitute the extreme inner parts of the spiral arms near the nucleus—features lost in normal half-tone reproductions.—D.]

[c] *Phil. Trans.* for 1795, page 68.

assume the brightness, and some of them perhaps also the size, of the sun; and the consequences that have been drawn from the observations given in my paper on the nature and construction of the sun, may be legitimately applied to the stars; whence it follows that stars, although surrounded by a luminous atmosphere, may be looked upon as so many opaque, habitable, planetary globes; differing from what we know of our own planets, only in their size, and by their intrinsically luminous appearance.

They also, like the planets, shine with differently coloured light. That of Arcturus and Aldebaran for instance, is as different from the light of Sirius and Capella, as that of Mars and Saturn is from the light of Venus and Jupiter. A still greater variety of coloured star-light has already been shewn to exist in many double stars, such as $\gamma$ Andromedæ, $\beta$ Cygni, and many more.[a] In my sweeps are also recorded the places of 9 deep garnet, 5 bright garnet, and 10 red coloured stars, of various small magnitudes from the 7th to the 12th.

By some experiments, on the light of a few of the stars of the first magnitude,[b] made in 1798, by a prism applied to the eye-glasses of my reflectors, adjustable to any angle and to any direction, I had the following analyses.

The light of Sirius consists of red, orange, yellow, green, blue, purple, and violet.

$\alpha$ Orionis contains the same colours, but the red is more intense, and the orange and yellow are less copious in proportion than they are in Sirius.

Procyon contains all the colours, but proportionally more blue and purple than Sirius.

Arcturus contains more red and orange and less yellow in proportion than Sirius.

Aldebaran contains much orange, and very little yellow.

$\alpha$ Lyræ contains much yellow, green, blue, and purple.[c]

The similarity of the general construction of the sun, the stars, and the

---

[a] See Catalogue of double stars *Phil. Trans.* for 1782, III. 5.   V. 5, &c.

[b] [Spectroscopy is of course a fundamental tool of modern astrophysics. Prismatic experiments on starlight were suggested to Herschel in 1783 by one Thomas Collinson who spent the night at Datchet. In spite of letters from Collinson (20 June 1783), Watson (31 August 1783), and Collinson again (5 December 1794), Herschel took little interest in making observations which he had no hope of interpreting.]

[c] [Herschel's qualitative descriptions of the spectra are in reasonable agreement with the spectral types: Sirius (A1), $\alpha$ Lyrae (A0), Procyon (F5) showing "all the colours" including violet; Aldebaran (K5), Arcturus (K0), and $\alpha$ Orionis (M2) more light in the red and orange.—D.]

planets, is also much supported by the periodical variations of the light of the stars observed in many of them;[a] for these variations can only be satisfactorily accounted for by admitting such stars to have a rotatory motion on their axes, like that which the sun and the planets are known to have.[b]

10. *Of the aggregation of Stars.*

11. *Of irregular Clusters.*

12. *Of Clusters variously extended and compressed.*

13. *Of Clusters of Stars of a peculiar description.*

14. *Of differently compressed Clusters of Stars.*

15. *Of the gradual concentration and insulation of Clusters of Stars.*

16. *Of globular Clusters of Stars.*[c]

17. *Of more distant globular Clusters of Stars.*[d]

18. *Of still more distant globular Clusters of Stars.*[e]

19. *Of a recurrence of the ambiguous limit of observation.*

In the 16th article I have given a description of the most magnificently constructed sidereal systems; and very little doubt can be entertained but that the objects of the 17th and 18th articles are of the same nature, and are only less beautiful in their appearance as they are gradually more remote. It has already been shewn in the 8th article, that in passing from faint nebulosity to the suspected sidereal condition, we cannot avoid meeting with ambiguous objects, to which I must now add, that the same critical situation will again occur, when from the distinctly sidereal appearance

[a] See MR. PIGOTT's Catalogue of variable stars *Phil. Trans.* for 1786, page 191.

[b] See Remarks on the rotatory motion of stars on their axes, *Phil. Trans.*, 1796, p. 456.

[c] [Articles 10–16 are accounts of galactic and globular clusters mostly fully resolved into stars by Herschel. See Plate 8, figs. 14–17.—D.]

[d] [Eight objects, comprising five globular clusters, one galactic cluster, one Sb, and one Sc galaxy.—D.]

[e] [Five objects, which Herschel correctly identifies as globular clusters although he had not seen the individual stars.—D.]

we endeavour to penetrate gradually farther into space. In consequence of this remark, it seems probable that among the numerous globular nebulæ which have been given in my last paper, many beautiful clusters of stars may lie concealed. To this we may add, that several of the great number of objects which have been given as stellar nebulæ, and are probably at a still greater distance from us, may be the last glimpses we can have of such clusters of stars as the 77th of the *Connoissance des Temps*,[a] which will nearly put on the stellar appearance when it is viewed in a very good common telescope.

This ambiguity, however, being the necessary consequence of the faintness or distance of objects, when seen through telescopes that are not sufficiently powerful to shew them as they are, will not affect any of the arguments that have been used to establish the existence of a clustering power, the effects of which have gradually been traced from the first indication of clustering stars, through irregular as well as through more artificially arranged clusters, up to the beautiful globular form.

The extended views I have taken, in this and my former papers, of the various parts that enter into the construction of the heavens, have prepared the way for a final investigation of the universal arrangement of all these celestial bodies in space; but as I am still engaged in a series of observations for ascertaining a scale whereby the extent of the universe, as far as it is possible for us to penetrate into space, may be fathomed, I shall conclude this paper by pointing out some inferences which the continuation of the action of the clustering power enables us to draw from the observations that have been given.

### 20. *Of the breaking up of the milky way.*

The milky way is generally represented in astronomical maps as an irregular zone of brightness encircling the heavens, and my star gages have proved its whitish tinge to arise from accumulated stars, too faint to be distinguished by the eye. The great difficulty of giving a true picture of it is a sufficient excuse for those who have traced it on a globe, or through the different constellations of an *Atlas Cælestis*, as if it were a uniform succession of brightness. It is, however, evident that, if ever it consisted of equally scattered stars, it does so no longer; for, by looking at it in a fine night, we may see its course between the constellations of Sagittarius and Perseus affected by not less than eighteen different shades of glimmering light, resembling the telescopic appearances of large easily resolvable nebulæ; but in addition to these general divisions, the observations detailed

[a] [M77=NGC 1068. Not a cluster of stars, but a Sb galaxy. It has a very bright small nucleus.—D.]

in the preceding pages of this paper, authorise us to anticipate the breaking up of the milky way, in all its minute parts, as the unavoidable consequence of the clustering power arising out of those preponderating attractions which have been shewn to be everywhere existing in its compass.

One hundred and fifty-seven instances have been given of clusters situated within the extent of the milky way, and their places are referred to in nine preceding articles. They may also be found in BODE's *Atlas Cœlestis*, whose delineation of this bright zone I have taken for a standard. To these must be added 68 more, which are in the less rich parts, or what may be called the vanishing borders of the milky way: for this immense stratum of stars does not break off abruptly, as generally represented in maps, but gradually becomes invisible to the eye when the stars are no longer sufficiently numerous to cause the impression of milkiness.

Now, since the stars of the milky way are permanently exposed to the action of a power whereby they are irresistibly drawn into groups, we may be certain that from mere clustering stars they will be gradually compressed through successive stages of accumulation, more or less resembling the state of some of the 263 objects by which, in the tenth and six succeeding articles, the operation of the clustering power has been laid open to our view, till they come up to what may be called the ripening period of the globular form, and total insulation; from which it is evident that the milky way must be finally broken up, and cease to be a stratum of scattered stars.

We may also draw a very important additional conclusion from the gradual dissolution of the milky way; for the state into which the incessant action of the clustering power has brought it at present, is a kind of chronometer that may be used to measure the time of its past and future existence; and although we do not know the rate of going of this mysterious chronometer, it is nevertheless certain, that since the breaking up of the parts of the milky way affords a proof that it cannot last for ever, it equally bears witness that its past duration cannot be admitted to be infinite.

# Chapter Five
# *The Final Fathoming*

THE first major task in astronomy that Herschel set himself was, as we have seen, to determine the distances of the stars from the Earth and so add a third dimension to sidereal astronomy. It was a problem to which he returned time and again, and which was to be the subject of his last two major papers, written when he was nearly eighty.

Ultimately, some sixteen years after Herschel's death, it was the triangulation method depending on the detection of annual parallax among the stars that established the first accurate stellar distances, when four astronomers applied their high-quality instruments to stars chosen because for various reasons they were suspected of being near—Bessel at Königsberg studying 61 Cygni because of its large proper motion, Struve at Dorpat observing Vega because of its brilliance, its considerable proper motion, and also its convenient position in the sky, and Henderson and Maclear at the Cape of Good Hope scrutinizing α Centauri, which had a large proper motion and was a binary describing in a short period what appears as a large orbit.

Herschel, however, had had little hope of succeeding with triangulation once his double-star method proved inconclusive, for although he always recognized distances calculated by triangulation as the desideratum, his own instruments were designed for magnification and space-penetration, not for exact measurement of stellar positions. Accordingly he had no alternative but to fall back on the measurement of starlight, to be interpreted on the 'brightness equals nearness' principle: that the ratio of the distances of two stars is (approximately) the inverse square of the ratio of their apparent brightnesses.

His problem was then a practical one, that of actually making quantitative comparisons of starlight. Other astronomers, on the hunt for variable stars, needed only qualitative comparisons— though here once again Herschel provided the "natural history" required on the grand scale, in six catalogues in which he carefully compared stars of similar brightnesses so that even slight variations in the brightness of a given star would upset the delicate comparisons listed.[1] But the determination of stellar distances called for precise, quantitative comparisons of brightness which Herschel might then translate into comparisons of distance.

The pioneer treatment of photometry, Pierre Bouguer's *Traité d'optique sur la gradation de la lumiere*,[2] had appeared in 1760 and was known to Herschel by 1780,[3] but the methods described were not easy to apply. Herschel was not alone in this predicament: in 1785 Edward Pigott explained in "Observations on a new variable star" that he had tried differently smoked glasses, variable diaphragms, varying the focusing, and adding light from outside the telescope, all without success.[4]

For his 1806 paper on the velocity of the solar motion, Herschel was still having to fall back on direct comparisons by eye. "I have tried", he wrote, "all the known, and many new ways of measuring the comparative light of the stars, and though I have not yet found one that will give a satisfactory result, it may still be possible to discover some method of mensuration preferable to the foregoing conclusions, which are only the result of repeated and accurate comparisons by the eye."[5]

At this period he was still unsure even of the answer to the elementary question of whether the traditional star magnitudes *directly* represented distance. As we saw (above, pp. 32–5), he had stated this as a postulate in his paper "On the Parallax of the Fixed Stars"; and when Maskelyne had pointed out that Michell reckoned a first-magnitude star to be 400 to 1000 times brighter than one of the sixth magnitude and so at about one-twentyfifth of the distance, and not one-sixth as Herschel supposed, Herschel had covered himself by saying that his postulate *defined* his magnitudes, and that he was not concerned with the traditional ones. Unfortunately the plain fact was that he simply could not measure these magnitudes he had defined, and until he could do so the postulate as applied to the traditional magnitudes would —if true—be a convenient substitute in the study of the brighter stars. But was it true?

Herschel, as we have seen (above, pp. 35–6), had been fascinated throughout his career by Halley's model according to which the distribution of the stars (including the Sun) throughout space is approximately uniform. As a test of the accuracy of this model, Halley had predicted from it the number of near stars and found that this satisfactorily approximated to the number of observed stars of the first magnitude; and in a casual manner he had applied a similar test for the second and third magnitudes.[6] In his early investigations Herschel believed that this model adequately corresponded to reality even out to the limits of the Milky Way, although as he became more aware of clustering among the stars he was forced to restrict more and more the application of this model.[7]

Convinced, then, that the model could validly be used as the basis of the study of the nearest stars, Herschel was in a position to test his postulate: the model predicted the number of stars at, say, six times the distance of Sirius; observation provided the number of stars actually of the traditional sixth magnitude; and comparison of these two numbers would therefore decide whether, as the postulate required, stars of the sixth magnitude were about six times as far as Sirius, or whether they were at some other distance.

Twice Herschel applied the test in a casual way. First, in 1796, he began the preface to his first catalogue of comparative brightness of stars by describing the model as a way of arriving at some (statistical) knowledge of the brightness of stars of the first two magnitudes, but only so as to show that this method is quite unsuitable for the detailed comparisons he required.[8]

Then, in 1800, in his study "On the power of penetrating into space by telescopes, with a determination of the extent of that power in natural vision and in telescopes",[9] he again faced the problem of the distance of the faintest (sixth- or seventh-magnitude) stars visible to the naked eye as compared with the distance of stars of the first magnitude. After a hasty comparison between the model and the observed figures for the first three magnitudes *only*, he hopefully decided that "no star, eight, nine, or at most ten times as far from us as Sirius, can possible be perceived by the natural eye".[10]

In 1806, however, he wrote: "I have thought it advisable to distinguish the stars that, from their lustre, may be called principal, and have limited their extent to the brightest of the second magnitude, on account of the uncertainty that remains about their progressive distances. For though it appears reasonable to allow that the bright stars of the second magnitude may be twice as far from us as those of the first, it will admit of some doubt whether this rule ought to be strictly followed up to the 3d, 4th, 5th, and 6th magnitude."[11] Possibly he had in mind Olbers's investigation of 1801,[12] where he had compared the light of Aldebaran with that of a sixth-magnitude star via a comparison of Mars and Uranus, and concluded that the difference between first and sixth magnitudes corresponded to a distance factor of 10. But any doubts Herschel may have felt did not prevent his going on to assign to Antares and Altair the absurdly precise comparative distances of 1·46 and 1·47 respectively, solely on the grounds of visual estimates of their magnitudes!

It was only in 1817, when, as we shall see, he had *already broken* the problem of quantitative comparisons of brightness and knew his postulate that traditional magnitudes directly represent distances was false, that Herschel at last calculated from the model the number of stars up to the seventh order of distances and counted the stars up to the seventh magnitude in Bode's catalogue (below, pp. 171–4). He found, for example, that the catalogue contained over six thousand stars of the sixth magnitude, whereas the model provided for only eight hundred and sixty-six at the sixth order of distance. "The result of this comparison therefore is, that if the order of the magnitudes could indicate the distance of the stars, it would denote at first a gradual, and afterwards a very abrupt condensation of them" —a preposterous situation.

Later in the paper (below, pp. 174–82), he showed on other grounds that natural vision extends to some fifteen times the distance of Sirius. He was now able to reverse the sequence of his earlier reasoning: instead of accepting the model and using it to test the postulate, now by substituting this new fact for the faulty postulate he could test the model. He found that the model predicted too few stars—but then, sixth- and seventh-magnitude stars were very unevenly scattered over the heavens, so that one already had other reasons for doubting the applicability of the model out to such distances.

It had been by a rather similar reversal of reasoning that Herschel had finally broken the problem of measuring differences in brightness. In his 1800 paper, he had defined the space-penetrating power of a telescope as the farthest distance at which the instrument could detect a star, taking as unity the space-penetrating power of the unaided eye. The main consideration was the amount of light the telescope collected from the star, and this in turn depended on the aperture of the instrument: for the 40-foot reflector the formula gave a penetrating power of 192. Even assuming the nearest stars to be at the minimum distances supplied by the failures-to-date of the triangulation method, this meant that the reflector could detect a cluster of five thousand stars at the respectable distance of nearly 12 million million million miles. Being in the mood for impressive figures, Herschel went on to estimate the time needed to sweep the sky with the monster, and found that with a magnification of 1000 it would take six hundred years![13]

Now the formula for penetrating power had been intended as a measure of his instruments: taking a particular instrument he calculated the maximum distance at which it could detect an hypothetical star. But there was no reason why it should not be applied the other way round: given an actually existing star, he could reduce the aperture of a suitable telescope until it was barely sufficient to detect the star, and then use the formula to calculate the penetrating power of the modified instrument, that is, the distance (or, more strictly, brightness) of the star.

In practice, of course, this experimenting with apertures had to be conducted with discretion if optical effects were not to invalidate the formula. And it is pleasing to see Herschel in his declining years still in full control of the experimental as well as the theoretical elements of his problem. He shows this in the way in which he modifies his technique to give more reliable results (below, pp. 175-7). Instead of limiting the aperture of one telescope to reduce the starlight to vanishing, he compares the star under examination with a known star by using two identical instruments (one directed to each of the stars) and limiting the aperture of one until both stars appear the same;[a] and so that it is not necessary to limit any one aperture excessively he compares stars of very different brightnesses via intermediate stars.

Herschel was now in a position to decide several long-standing issues. Whereas in 1806 he had had to guess the com-

[a] Surprisingly, Herschel had hinted at this technique in 1794: "Now if we would leave as much room between each of these stars as there is between the sun and Sirius, we must place these clusters 42104 times as far from us as that star is from the sun. But in order to bring down the lustre of Sirius to that of an equal star placed at such a distance, I ought to reduce the aperture of my 20-feet telescope to less than two-and-twenty-hundredth part of an inch. . . ." (Phil. Trans., LXXXV (1795), 69-70; Dreyer, I, 483). The method of measuring starlight by limiting apertures had been proposed as long ago as 1771 by J. S. Bailly in "Mémoire sur les inégalités de la lumière des satellites de Jupiter", Mémoires de l'Académie Royale des Sciences for 1771, 580-667.

parative brightnesses of the first-magnitude stars, now he could actually measure them. Whereas in 1800 he had supposed that Sirius could not be detected by the unaided eye at "eight, nine, or at most ten times" its present distance, now he could *demonstrate* that the correct figure for first-magnitude stars was about twelve (below, p. 180)—a result that is substantially correct. In 1785 he had believed his instruments to reach the limits of the Milky Way at some 497 times the distance of Sirius (above, p. 90); now when he examined the Galaxy with increasing space-penetrating powers he was always left with the impression of more distant stars yet to be detected, even when the 40-foot was at full stretch, so that the Milky Way must extend more than 2300 times the distance of a first-magnitude star (below, p. 186): it was, as he put it in 1818, "fathomless".[14]

# Astronomical Observations, and Experiments Tending to Investigate the Local Arrangement of the Celestial Bodies in Space.[a]

## Read June 19, 1817.

THE construction of the heavens, in which the real place of every celestial object in space is to be determined, can only be delineated with precision, when we have the situation of each heavenly body assigned in three dimensions, which in the case of the visible universe may be called length, breadth, and depth; or longitude, latitude, and Profundity.

The angular positions of the stars and other celestial objects, as they are given in astronomical catalogues, and represented upon globes, or laid down in maps, enable us, in a clear night, to find them by the eye or to view them in a telescope; for, in order to direct an instrument to them, a superficial place consisting of only two dimensions is sufficient; but although the line in which they are to be seen is thus pointed out to us, their distance from the eye in that line remains unknown; and unless a proper method for obtaining the profundity of objects can be found, their longitude and latitude will not enable us to assign their local arrangement in space.

[a] [*Phil. Trans.*, CVII (1817), 302–31.]

With regard to objects comparatively very near to us, astronomers have completely succeeded by the method of parallaxes. The distance of the sun; the dimensions of the orbits of the planets and of their satellites; the diameters of the sun, the moon, and the rest of the bodies belonging to the solar system, as well as the distances of comets, have all been successfully ascertained. The parallax of the fixed stars has also been an object of attention; and although we have hitherto had no satisfactory result from the investigation, the attempt has at least so far succeeded as to give us a most magnificent idea of the vast expansion of the sidereal heavens, by showing that probably the whole diameter of the earth's orbit, at the distance of a star of the first magnitude, does not subtend an angle of more than a single second of a degree, if indeed it should amount to so much; with regard to more remote objects, however, such as the stars of smaller size, highly compressed clusters of stars and nebulæ, the parallactic method can give us no assistance.

### I. *Of the local situation of the stars of the heavens.*

The superficial situation of the stars having already been carefully assigned in the catalogues of astronomers, it will be proper to examine how far the arrangement of the stars into a certain order of magnitudes can assist us to determine their local situation.

When we look at the heavens in a clear night, and observe the different lustre of the stars, we are impressed with a certain idea of their different magnitudes; and when our estimation is confined to their appearance only, we shall be justified in saying, for instance, that Arcturus is larger than Aldebaran; the principle on which the stars are classed is, therefore, entirely founded on their apparent magnitude, or brightness. Now, as it was thought convenient to arrange all the stars which in fine weather may be seen by the eye into seven classes, the brightest were called of the first, and the rest according to their gradually diminishing lustre, of the 2d, 3d, 4th, 5th, 6th, and 7th magnitudes. Then, since it is evident that we cannot mean to affirm that the stars of the 5th, 6th, and 7th magnitudes are really smaller than those of the 1st, 2d, or 3d, we must ascribe the cause of the difference in the apparent magnitudes of the stars to a difference in their relative distances from us; and on account of the great number of stars contained in each class, we must also allow that the stars of each succeeding magnitude, beginning from the first, are one with another farther from us than those of the magnitude immediately preceding. It may therefore be said, that since in our catalogues the magnitudes are added to the two dimensions which give the superficial place of the stars, we have also at least a presumptive value of the third dimension; but admitting that the naked eye can see stars as far from us as those of the seventh magnitude, this presumptive value, which can only point out their relative situation, will afford us no information about the real distance at which they are placed.

## II. *Of a standard by which the relative arrangement of the stars may be examined.*

It is evident, that when we propose to examine how the stars of the heavens are arranged, we ought to have a certain standard of reference; and this I believe may be had by comparing their distribution to a certain properly modified equality of scattering. Now, the equality I shall here propose, does not require that the stars should be at equal distances from each other; nor is it necessary that all those of the same nominal magnitude should be equally distant from us. It consists in allotting a certain equal portion of space to every star, in consequence of which we may calculate how many stars any given extent of space should contain. This definition of equal scattering agrees so far with observation, that it admits, for instance, Sirius, Arcturus, and Aldebaran to be put into the same class, notwithstanding their very different lustre will not allow us to suppose them to be at equal distances from us; but its chief advantage will be, that instead of the order of magnitudes into which our catalogues have arranged the stars, it will give us an order of distances, which may be used for ascertaining the local distribution of the heavenly bodies in space.

To explain this arrangement, let a circle be drawn with any given radius about the point S fig. 10, and with 3, 5, 7, 9, &c. times the same radius draw circles, or circular arcs, about the same centre. Then if a portion of space equal to the solid contents of a sphere, represented by the circle S, be allotted to each star, the circles, or circular arcs drawn about it will denote spheres containing the stars of their own order, and of all the orders belonging to the included spheres, and on the supposition of an equality of scattering, the number of stars of any given order may be had by inspection of the figure, which contains all the numbers that are required for the purpose; for those in front of the diagram express the diameters of spherical figures. The first row of numbers enclosed between the successive arcs, are the cubes of the diameters; the next column expresses the order of the central distances; and the last gives the difference between the cube numbers of any order and the cube of the next enclosed order.

The use to be made of these columns of numbers is by inspection to determine how many stars of any particular order there ought to be if the stars were equally scattered. For instance, let it be required how many stars

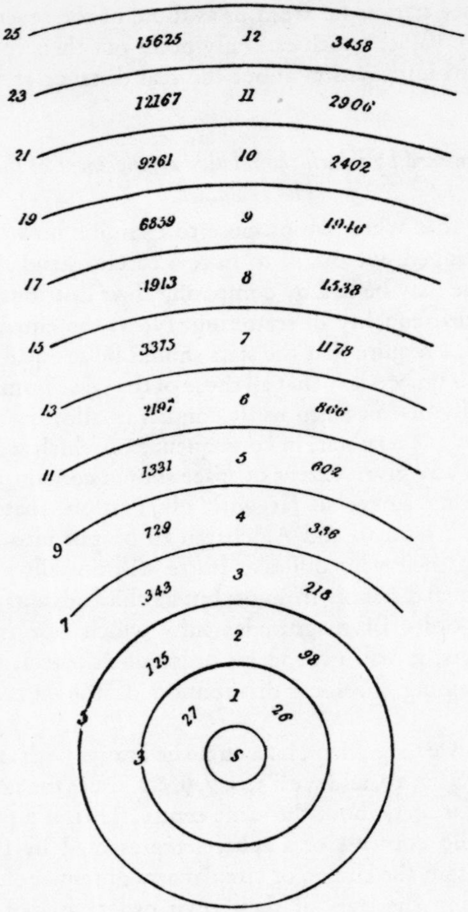

FIG. 10.

Herschel's calculation of the number of stars to be expected at different distances from the Sun, on the assumption that the stars are uniform in brightness and uniformly distributed in space. If the nearest stars are at distance 1 from the Sun, then the Sun is "allotted" the space up to distance $\frac{1}{2}$, and the nearest stars share the space from $\frac{1}{2}$ to $\frac{3}{2}$. This space is $27 - 1 = 26$ times the space allotted to the Sun, and so there should be 26 such stars. Similarly, the next nearest stars are at distance 2 and together share the space from distance $\frac{3}{2}$ to $\frac{5}{2}$. This space is $125 - 27 = 98$ times the space allotted to the Sun, and so there should be 98 such stars.

there should be of the 4th order. Then No. 4, in the column of the orders points out a sphere of nine times the diameter of the central one, and shows that it would contain 729 stars; but as this sphere includes all the stars of the 3d, 2d, and 1st order as well as the sun, their number will be the sum of all the stars contained in the next inferior sphere amounting to 343; which being taken from 729 leaves 386 for the space allotted to those of the 4th order of distances.

### III. *Comparison of the order of magnitudes with the order of distances.*

With a view to throw some light upon the question, in what manner the stars are scattered in space, we may now compare their magnitudes, as we find them assigned in MR. BODE's extensive catalogue of stars, with the order of their distances which has been explained.

The catalogue I have mentioned contains 17 stars of the 1st magnitude; but in my figure of the order of the distances we find their number to be 26.

The same catalogue has 57 stars of the 2d magnitude; but the order of distances admits 98.

Of the third magnitude the catalogue has 206, and the order of distances will admit 218.

The number of the stars of the 4th magnitude is by the catalogue 454, and by the order of distances 386.

Before I proceed, it may be proper to remark, that, by these four classifications of the stars into magnitudes, it appears already, that, on account of the great difference in the lustre of the brightest stars, many of them have been put back into the second class; and that the same visible excess of light has also occasioned many of the stars of the next degree of brightness to be put into the third class; but the principle of the visibility of the difference in brightness would have less influence with the gradually diminishing lustre of the stars, so that the number of those of the third magnitude would come nearly up to those of the third distance. And as the difference in the light of small stars is less visible than in the larger ones, we find that the catalogue has admitted a greater number of stars of the 4th magnitude than the 4th order of distances points out; this may, however, be owing to taking in the stars that were thrown back from the preceding orders; and a remarkable coincidence of numbers seems to confirm this account of the arrangement of the stars into magnitudes. For the total number of the catalogued stars of the 1st, 2d, 3d, and 4th magnitudes, with the addition of the sun, is 735; and the number contained in the whole sphere of the 4th distance is 729.

Now the distinguishable difference of brightness becoming gradually less as the stars are smaller, the effect of the principle of classification will be, as indeed we find it in the 5th, 6th, and 7th classes, that fainter stars must be admitted into them than the order of distances points out.

The catalogue contains 1161 stars of the 5th magnitude, whereas the 5th order of distances has only room for 602.

Of the 6th magnitude the catalogue contains not less than 6103 stars, but the 6th order of distances will admit only 866.

And lastly, the same catalogue points out 6146 stars of the 7th magnitude, while the number of stars that can be taken into the 7th order of distances is only 1178.

The result of this comparison therefore is, that if the order of magnitudes could indicate the distance of the stars, it would denote at first a gradual, and afterwards a very abrupt condensation of them; but that, considering the principle on which the stars are classed, their arrangement into magnitudes can only apply to certain relative distances, and show that taking the stars of each class one with another, those of the succeeding magnitudes are farther from us than the stars of the preceding order.

## IV. *Of a criterion for ascertaining the Profundity, or local situation of celestial objects in space.*

It has been shown that the presumptive distances of the stars pointed out by their magnitudes can give us no information of their real situation in space. The statement, however, that one with another the faintest stars are at the greatest distance from us, seems to me so forcible, that I believe it may serve for the foundation of an experimental investigation.

It will be admitted, that the light of a star is inversely as the square of its distance; if therefore we can find a method by which the degree of light of any given star may be ascertained, its distance will become a subject of calculation. But in order to draw valid consequences from experiments made upon the brightness of different stars, we shall be obliged to admit, that one with another the stars are of a certain physical generic size and brightness, still allowing that all such deviations may exist, as generally take place among the individuals belonging to the same species.

There may be some difference in the intrinsic brightness of starlight: that of highly coloured stars may differ from the light of the bluish white ones; but in remarkable cases allowances may be made.

With regard to size, or diameter, we are perhaps more liable to error; but the extensive catalogue which has already been consulted, contains not less than 14,144 stars of the seven magnitudes that have been adverted to; it may therefore be presumed that any star promiscuously chosen for an experiment, out of such a number, is not likely to differ much from a certain mean size of them all.

At all events it will be certain that those stars the light of which we can experimentally prove to be $\frac{1}{4}$, $\frac{1}{9}$, $\frac{1}{16}$, $\frac{1}{25}$, $\frac{1}{36}$, and $\frac{1}{49}$ of the light of any certain star of the 1st magnitude, must be 2, 3, 4, 5, 6, and 7 times as far from us as the standard star, provided the condition of the stars should come up to the supposed mean state of diameter and lustre of the standard star, and of this, when many equalisations are made, there is at least a great probability in favour.

## V. *Of the equalisation of starlight.*

In my sweeps of the heavens, the idea of ascertaining the Profundity of space to which our telescopes might reach, gave rise to an investigation of their space penetrating power; and finding that this might be calculated with reference to the extent of the same power of which the unassisted eye is capable, there always remained a desideratum of some sure method by which this might be ascertained.

Of various experiments I have long ago tried, the equalisation of starlight, which about four years ago I began to put into execution, appeared to be the most practicable. A description of the apparatus and the method of making use of it is as follows.

Of ten highly finished mirrors I selected two of an equal diameter and focal length, and placed them in two similarly fitted up seven feet telescopes. When they were completely adjusted, I directed them both, with a magnifying power of 118, to the same star, for instance, Arcturus: and upon trial I found the light not only of this, but of every other star to which they were directed, perfectly equal in both telescopes.

The two instruments, when I viewed the stars, were placed one a little before the other, and so near together that it would require little more than one second of time to look from one into the other. This convenient situation of the instruments is of great importance. The impression of the light made by the view of one star should be succeeded as soon as possible by the view of the other; and these alternate inspections should also be many times repeated, in order to take away some little advantage which the last view of a bright object has over that immediately preceding.

In comparing the light of one star with that of another, I laid it down as a principle, that no estimation but that of perfect equality should be admitted; and as the equal action of the instruments was now ascertained, I calculated the diameters of several apertures to be given to one of the telescopes as a standard, so that the other, called the equalising telescope, might be employed, with all its aperture unconfined, to examine a variety of stars, till one of them was found whose light was equal to that of the star to which the standard telescope was directed.[a]

In order to be sufficiently accurate in the calculation of the diameter of the limiting apertures, I thought it necessary to take into consideration not only the obstruction of incident light occasioned by the interposition of the small mirror, but also of the arm to which it is fastened, and proceeded as follows:

If A be the diameter of the large mirror; $b$ that of the small one; $\frac{A-b}{2}$ the length of the arm; $t$ its thickness; $\pi$ the circumference, diameter being unity; $x$ an assumed quantity for finding the correction; A′ the aperture corrected for the interposition of the arm; L the light of the equalising telescope; $p$ the proportion of the light required for the standard telescope; D the diameter of an aperture to give that light; D′ the diameter corrected for the interposition of the arm.

Then will the diameters of the limiting apertures be had by the following equations. $\frac{A-b}{2} \times t = \pi A x$; $\frac{A-b}{\pi A} \times t = 2x$; $A - 2x = A'$; $A'^2 - b^2 = L$; $pL = D^2 - b^2$; $\sqrt{pL + b^2} = D$; $\frac{D-b}{\pi D} \times t = 2\gamma$; $D + 2\gamma = D'$ the required diameter.

In the calculation of a set of apertures for the intended purpose, I admitted none that gave less than $\frac{1}{4}$ of the light; for by a greater contraction of the aperture of the mirror, an increase of the spurious diameters would render a judgment of equality liable to deception;[b] when therefore a star of the third order of distances was to be found, I rejected the direct way of reducing a star of the first order to $\frac{1}{9}$ of its light, but selected a star previously ascertained to be of the second order; and by taking $\frac{4}{9}$ of its light, the equalising telescope, with all its light, was used to examine all such stars as appeared likely to give the required equality, till one of them was found; nor was it necessary to have a great number of limiting

[a] I preferred the limitation of the light by circular apertures to the method of obtaining it by the approach or recess of two opposite rectangular plates, in order to avoid the inflections which take place in the angles.

[b] This was fully proved by the following experiment. July 27, 1813, I viewed Arcturus in a 10 feet reflector; first with all its light; next with circular diaphragms, which confined its aperture to $\frac{1}{4}$, $\frac{1}{9}$, $\frac{1}{16}$, $\frac{1}{25}$, $\frac{1}{36}$, and $\frac{1}{49}$ of it; but I found that the different spurious diameters, arising from the smallness of the apertures, made estimations of what is generally called the magnitude of the stars impossible.

See also experiments on the spurious diameters of the celestial objects, *Phil. Trans.* for 1805, page 40.

apertures, as it soon appeared that with eight or ten of them I could have many different gradations of light, which would ascertain even fractional degrees, and reach as far as the stars of any order of distances I could expect to be visible to the unassisted eye.

This method of equalising the light of the stars, easy as it may appear, is nevertheless subject to great difficulties; for as the brightness of a star is affected by its situation, with regard to the ambient light of the heavens, the stars to be equalised should, if possible, be in nearly the same region. When the sun is deep under the horizon, this is however not of so much consequence as the altitude of the star to be equalised, which ought to be as nearly as possible equal to that of the standard star. At great elevations some difference in the altitudes of the stars to be equalised may be admitted; but, if they are far from each other, the circumstance of the equal illumination of the heavens, and the equal clearness of the air, must still be attended to.

### VI. *Of the extent of natural vision.*

The method of equalising star light may be rigorously applied to ascertain the extent of natural vision; for in this case it will not be required that the star on which the experiment is tried, should be of the same size or diameter with the standard star; nor is it necessary that the intrinsic brightness of the light of the two stars should be the same in both. It will be sufficient, that the star we choose for an equalisation is one of the smallest that are still visible to the natural eye. It is also to be understood that, till we can have a well ascertained value of the parallax of any one star of the first magnitude, the extent of natural vision can only be given in a measure of which the distance of the standard star is the unit.

The following equalisations were made in August and December 1813, and February 1814, and are given as a specimen of the method I have pursued.

Taking Arcturus for the standard of an experiment, I directed the telescope, with one quarter of its light, upon it; while the equalising telescope, with all its light, was successively set upon such stars as I supposed might be at double the distance of the standard star; which, as Arcturus is a star of the first magnitude, I expected to find among those of the second.

The first I tried was $\beta$ (FL. 53) Pegasi, but I found it not quite bright enough.

The light of $\alpha$ Andromedæ, which next I tried, was nearly equalised to that of Arcturus; and the observation being repeated on a different night gave it equal.

Now as in these experiments the standard star is supposed to be one of the first order of distances, it follows that, if Arcturus were put at twice its distance from us, it would then appear like α Andromedæ, as a star of the 2d magnitude, and would also at the same time be really a star of the 2d order of distances.

In order to obtain some other stars whose light might be equalised by one quarter the light of Arcturus, I tried many different ones, and found among them α Polaris, γ Ursæ, and δ Cassiopeæ. These stars therefore may also be put into the class of those whose light is equal to the stars of the second order of the distance of Arcturus.

For the purpose of ascertaining the extent of natural vision, it will not be necessary here to give the equalisation of stars of the 3d, 5th, 6th, or 7th order of distances; but taking now the light of one of the stars of the 2d order of distances for a standard, I tried many that might be expected to have the required light, and found that when α Andromedæ, with its light reduced to one quarter, was in the standard telescope, the equalising one gave μ (FL. 48) Pegasi for a star of the 4th order of distances. That is to say, the equalisation proved that, if Arcturus were placed at four times its distance from us, we should see it as a star of the 4th magnitude, and also as one of the 4th order of distances.

Proceeding in the same manner with μ Pegasi taken as a standard, I found that its light reduced to ¼ was equal to that of q (FL. 70) Pegasi, when seen in the equalising telescope; and that consequently Arcturus, removed to 8 times its present distance from us, would put on the appearance of a star which in our catalogues is called of the 5th or 6th magnitude, but which would in fact be of the 8th order of distances.

As the foregoing experiments can only show that a star of the light of Arcturus might be removed to 8 times its distance, and still remain visible to the naked eye as a star of between the 5th and 6th magnitude; it will be proper to take also other stars of the first magnitude for the original standards.

For instance, if we begin from Capella as the standard star, we may with ¼ of its light equalise β Aurigæ and β Tauri, which stars will therefore be of the 2d order of distances. With ¼ of the light of β Tauri we equalise ζ Tauri and ι Aurigæ; they will then be of the 4th order. With ¼ of the light of ι Aurigæ we can equalise e Persei and H Geminorum which will be of the 8th order. And with $\frac{16}{25}$ of the light of H Geminorum we equalise d Geminorum, which makes it a star of the 10th order. That is to say, if Capella were successively removed to 2, 4, 8 and 10 times the distance at which it is from us, it would then have the appearance of the stars which have been named.

A similar deduction may be made from α Lyræ, as $\frac{1}{4}$ of its light equalises it with β Tauri; for it will be α Lyræ 1, β Tauri 2, ι Aurigæ 4, H Geminorum 8, and d Geminorum 10: the numbers annexed to the stars expressing their orders of distances in terms of the distance of α Lyræ from us.

To find stars of the intermediate orders of distances, the following Table gives the proportional light that should be used with the star which is made the standard; for instance, a star of the 2d order of distances, with $\frac{4}{9}$ of its light, will equalise a star of the 3d order; $\frac{9}{25}$ of the light of a star of the 3d order of distances will give one of the 5th order, and so on.

| A star of the order of distances. | With the proportion of its light. | Gives one of the order of distances. |
|---|---|---|
| 1 | $\frac{1}{4}$ | 2 |
| 2 | $\frac{4}{9}$ | 3 |
| | $\frac{1}{4}$ | 4 |
| 3 | $\frac{9}{25}$ | 5 |
| | $\frac{1}{4}$ | 6 |
| 4 | $\frac{16}{49}$ | 7 |
| | $\frac{1}{4}$ | 8 |
| 5 | $\frac{25}{81}$ | 9 |
| | $\frac{1}{4}$ | 10 |
| 6 | $\frac{36}{121}$ | 11 |
| | $\frac{1}{4}$ | 12 |

Some other proportions of light useful for fractional distances are $\frac{9}{16}$, $\frac{16}{52}$, $\frac{36}{49}$, $\frac{64}{81}$, and $\frac{100}{121}$.

The results of equalisations that are made with different standard stars, may be connected together by an equalisation of the standards; by which means many different sets may be brought to support each other. For instance, Capella with $\frac{36}{49}$ of its light is of an equal lustre with Procyon, which therefore is of the $1\frac{1}{6}$ order of Capella, and Sirius with $\frac{16}{49}$ of its light is also of an equal lustre with Procyon, which consequently, with regard to Sirius, is of the $1\frac{3}{4}$ order; then, by compounding, it follows that Capella to Sirius is a star of the $1\frac{1}{2}$ order, and from this we obtain the following series. Sirius 1, Capella $1\frac{1}{2}$, Procyon $1\frac{3}{4}$, β Tauri 3, ι Aurigæ 6, H Geminorum 12, and d Geminorum 15. By this connection we shall be able to obtain an equalisation of the same ultimate star with all the standards; for if Sirius must be removed to the 15th order, to appear as faint as *d* Geminorum; and if Capella, and also α Lyræ must be removed to the 10th order of distances to appear as faint as the same star, then any star of the size and brightness of Sirius, Capella, and α Lyræ must generally appear as faint as *d* Geminorum, when it is removed to nearly 12 times its distance; and the more stars of the first order are admitted in these general equalisations reduced to the same faint star, the more will the probability of the result be extended. Now as *d* Geminorum is a star of the 6th magnitude, we may expect that a still fainter visible star will give a somewhat greater extent to the reach of the natural eye; if however I take its vision, including other stars of the 1st magnitude, to extend to the 12th order of distances, there will probably be no material error, at least none but what a diligent astronomer, who is provided with the necessary apparatus, may correct by observation.

But the extent of natural vision is not limited to the light of solitary stars only; the united lustre of a number of them will become visible when the stars themselves cannot be seen. For instance, the milky way; the bright spot in the sword handle of Perseus; the cluster north of η and H Geminorum; the cluster south of FL. 6 and 9 Aquilæ; the cluster south of η Herculis, and the cluster north preceding ε Pegasi. But their distances cannot be ascertained by the method of equalising starlight: their probable situation in space may however be deduced from telescopic observations.

To these very faintly visible objects may be added two of a different nature, namely, the nebulosity in the sword of Orion, and that in the girdle of Andromeda.

## VII. *Of the extent of telescopic vision.*

The powers of telescopes to penetrate into the Profundity of space is the result of the quantity of light they collect and send to the eye in a state fit for vision. The method of calculating the quantity of this power has been fully explained in a Paper read before the Royal Society, November 21, 1799; and the formulæ which have been given in that Paper have already been applied to show to what extent this power has been carried in the telescopes I used for astronomical observations. The calculated results, however, give this power only in reference to that of natural vision, and the uncertainty in which we were left with regard to its extent, was equally thrown over that of telescopic vision.

The equalisation of starlight, when carried to a proper degree of accuracy, will do away with the cause of the error to which the telescopic extent of vision has been unavoidably subject; we may therefore safely apply this vision to measure the Profundity of sidereal objects that are far beyond the reach of the natural eye; but for this purpose the powers of penetrating into space of the telescopes that are to be used must be reduced to what may be called gaging powers; and as the formula $\dfrac{\sqrt{x \cdot A^2 - b^2}}{a}$[a] gives the whole quantity of the space penetrating power, a reduction to any inferior power $p$, may be made by the expression $\sqrt{\dfrac{p^2 a^2}{x} + b^2} = A$; when the aperture is then limited to the calculated value of A, the telescopes will have the required gaging power. Or we may prepare a regular set of apertures to serve for trials, and find the gaging powers they give to the telescope by the original formula.

In the formula by which the required apertures for the gaging powers were calculated, $a$ has been put equal to two tenths of an inch, and to show that this assumption is founded upon observation, I give the following extract from my astrononomical Journal.

Dec. 27, 1801. I looked at α Lyræ with one eye shut and the other guarded by a slip of brass with holes of various sizes in it. Through the hole which was 0·28 inch in diameter, I saw the star just as well as without the limiting diaphragm, which shows that the opening of the pupil of the eye does not exceed 0·28 inch.

I tried the same star through 0·24 and still saw it equally well. I tried next 0·21 and still saw it as well.

The slip of brass was held as close to the eye as possible. The next I tried was 0·17 in diameter, and through this I could perceive a small deficiency of light, so that the opening of the pupil exceeds 0·17 inch. The night is hardly dark enough yet for great accuracy.

Having been out long in the dark, and trying the same experiment upon many different large and small stars, they all concur to show that 0·21 does not sensibly stop any light; but that less does certainly render the object rather less luminous; so that the opening may be put at two-tenths of an inch in my eye.

VIII. *Application of the extent of natural and telescopic vision to the probable arrangement of the celestial bodies in space.*

When the extent of natural and telescopic vision is to be applied to investigate the distance of celestial objects, the result can only have a high degree of probability; for it will then be necessary to admit a certain physical generic size and brightness of the stars. But when two hypotheses are proposed to explain a certain phenomenon, that which will most naturally account for it ought to be preferred as being the most probable.

[a] See *Phil. Trans.* for 1800, page 66 [$a$ is the 'aperture of the eye'].

Now as the different magnitudes of the stars may be ascribed to a physical difference in their size and lustre, and may also be owing to the greater distance of the fainter ones, we cannot think it probable that all those of the 5th, 6th and 7th magnitude, should be gradually of a smaller physical construction than those of the 1st, 2d, and 3d; but shall, on the contrary, be fairly justified in concluding that, in conformity with all the phenomena of vision, the greater faintness of those stars is owing to their greater distance from us. The average size and brightness of several stars of the first magnitude being also taken as a standard, in the manner that has been shown, the conclusion drawn from different series of equalisations will support one another; so that we shall be able to say, a distant celestial object is so far from us, provided the stars of which it is composed are of a size and lustre equal to the size and lustre of such stars as Sirius, Arcturus, Capella, Lyra, Rigel, and Procyon, &c.

I proceed now to consider some conclusions that may be drawn from a known extent of natural vision, a very obvious one of which is, that all the visible stars are probably contained within a sphere of the 12th order of distances. Now as on the principle of equal scattering, we should see about 15625 of them, it may be remarked that the stars of the catalogue, including all those of the 7th magnitude, amount to 14144, which agrees sufficiently well with the calculated number; but the next inference is, that if they were equally scattered, there would be 2402 of the 10th, 2906 of the 11th, and 3458 of the 12th order of distances, which added together amount only to 8766, whereas the number of stars of the 6th and 7th magnitudes that must come into these three orders, is not less than 12249, which would indicate that the stars in the higher order of distances are more compressed than they are in the neighbourhood of the sun; but from astronomical observations, we also know that the stars of the 6th and 7th magnitude are very sparingly scattered over many of the constellations, and that consequently the stars which belong to the 10th, 11th, and 12th order of distances, are not only more compressed than those in the neighbourhood of the sun, but that moreover their compression in different parts of the heavens must be very unequal.

## IX. *Of the construction and extent of the milky way.*

Of all the celestial objects consisting of stars not visible to the eye, the milky way is the most striking; its general appearance, without applying a telescope to it, is that of a zone surrounding our situation in the solar system, in the shape of a succession of differently condensed patches of brightness, intermixed with others of a fainter tinge.

To enumerate a partial series of them, we have a very bright patch under the arrow of Sagittarius; another in the Scutum Sobiescii; between these two there are three unequally bright places; north preceding α, β and γ Aquilæ is a bright patch; between Aquila and the Scutum are two very faint places; a long faint place follows the shoulder of Ophiuchus; near β Cygni is a bright place; near γ is another, and a third near α. A smaller brightish place follows in the succession of the milky way, and a large one towards Cassiopea. A faint place is on one side; a second towards Cassiopea, and a third is within that constellation; a very bright place is in the sword handle of Perseus; and α and γ Cassiopeæ inclose a dark spot.

The breadth of the milky way appears to be very unequal. In a few places it does not exceed five degrees; but in several constellations it is extended from ten to sixteen. In its course it runs nearly 120 degrees in a divided clustering stream, of which the two branches between Serpentarius and Antinous are expanded over more than 22 degrees.

That the sun is within its plane may be seen by an observer in the latitude of about 60 degrees; for when at 100 degrees of right ascension the milky way is in the east, it will at the same time be in the west at 280; while in its meridional situation it will pass through Cassiopea in the Zenith, and through the constellation of the cross in the Nadir.

From this survey of the milky way by the eye I shall now proceed to show what appears to be its construction by applying to it the extent of telescopic vision; but as I had prepared a gradually increasing series of reductions of the space-penetrating powers of my instruments for the purpose of measuring the Profundity of sidereal objects not visible to the eye, which I have called gaging powers, it will be necessary to give the following account of it.

From the formula which has been given, I calculated a set of apertures, which by limiting the light of the finder of my seven feet reflector would reduce its space-penetrating power to the low gaging powers 2, 3, and 4. I then limited in the same manner the space-penetrating power of my night glass, by using calculated apertures such as would give the gaging powers 5, 6, 7 and 8. From the space-penetrating power of the 7 feet reflector, I obtained by limitation the successive gaging powers 9, 10 and upwards to 17. And lastly, by limiting the space-penetrating power of my 10 feet reflector, I carried the gaging powers from 17 to 28.

For the purpose of trying these powers, I selected the bright spot in the sword handle of Perseus, as being probably a protuberant part of the milky way, in which it is situated. Its altitude at the time of observation was about 30 degrees, and no star in it was visible.

In the finder with the gaging power 2, I saw many stars; and admitting the eye to reach to stars at the distance of the 12th order, we may conclude that the small stars which were visible with this low power, are such as contribute to the brightness of the spot, and that their situation is probably from between the 12th to the 24th order of distances; at least we are certain, that if stars of the size and lustre of Sirius, Arcturus, Capella, &c. were removed into the Profundity of space which I have mentioned, they would then appear like the stars I saw with the gaging power of the finder. I then changed this power from 2 to 3, and saw more stars than before; and changing it again from 3 to 4, a still greater number of them became visible. The situation of these additional stars was consequently between the 24th, 36th, and 48th order of distances.

With the gaging power 5 of the night glass I saw a great number of stars; with 6, more stars and whitishness became visible; with 7, more stars with resolvable whitishness were seen; and with 8, still more. The stars that gradually made their appearance, therefore, were probably scattered over the space between the 48th and 96th order of distances.

In the 7 feet reflector, with the gaging powers 9 and 10, I saw a great number of stars; with 11 and 12, a greater number of stars and resolvable whitishness were seen; with 13 and 14, the number of visible stars was increased, and was so again with 15; with 16 and 17 in addition to the visible stars, there were many too faint to be distinctly perceived. These gages therefore extend the space over which the additional stars were scattered from the 96th to the 204th order of distances.

With a 10 feet reflector, reduced to a gaging power of 18, I saw a great number of stars: they were of very different magnitudes, and many whitish appearances were so faint that their consisting of stars remained doubtful. The power 19, which next I used, verified the reality of several suspected stars, and increased the lustre of the former ones. With 20, 22, and 25, the same progressive verifications of suspected stars took place, and those which had been verified by the preceding powers, received subsequent additional illumination. With the whole space-penetrating power of the instrument, which is 28·67, the extremely faint stars in the field of view acquired more light, and many still fainter suspected whitish points could not be verified for want of a still higher gaging power. The stars which filled the field of view were of every various order of telescopic magnitudes, and, as appears by these observations, were probably scattered over a space extending from the 204th to the 344th order of distances.

As the power of the 10 feet reflector could not reach farther into space, I shall have recourse to some of my numerous observations made with the 20 feet telescope. In addition to 683 gages already published,[a] above 400

[a] See *Phil. Trans.* for 1785, p. 221 [above, p. 88].

more have been taken in various parts of the heavens, but with regard to these gages, which on a supposition of an equality of scattering were looked upon as gages of distances, I have now to remark that, although a greater number of stars in the field of view is generally an indication of their greater distance from us, these gages, in fact, relate more immediately to the scattering of the stars, of which they give us a valuable information, such as will prove the different richness of the various regions of the heavens.

July 30, 1785. Right ascension 19$^h$ 4'. Polar distance 87° 5'. The milky way is extremely rich in stars that are too small for the gage.

Dec. 7, 1785. Right ascension 5$^h$ 33'. Polar distance 66° 6'. There are about 66 stars in the field of view, and many more so extremely small as not to admit of being gaged.

Sept. 20, 1786. Right ascension 20$^h$ 40'. Polar distance 54° 36'. There are about 80 stars in a quadrant, or 320 in the field of view, besides many more too small to be distinctly seen.

Oct. 14, 1787. Right ascension 21$^h$ 57'. Polar distance from 35° 18' to 38° 50'. In this part of the heavens the large stars seem to be of the 9th and 10th magnitude. The small ones are gradually less till they escape the eye, so that appearances here favour the idea of a succeeding, more distant clustering part of the milky way.

Sept. 18, 1784. Right ascension 20$^h$ 8'. Polar distance from 70° 9' to 72° 49'. The end of the stratum of the stars of the milky way cannot be seen.[a]

By these observations it appears that the utmost stretch of the space-penetrating power of the 20 feet telescope could not fathom the Profundity of the milky way, and that the stars which were beyond its reach must have been farther from us than the 900dth order of distances.

I am far from limiting the milky way to the extent deduced from these observations; but as even the distance which has been stated may appear doubtful, I must repeat the argument which has been used with stars visible to the eye, but which now is greatly supported by telescopic vision. If the stars of the 5th, 6th, and 7th magnitudes cannot be supposed to be gradually of a smaller physical size and brightness than those of the 1st, 2d, and 3d, how much less can a supposition be admitted that would require that the stars, which by a long series of gaging powers have been proved to make their gradual telescopic appearance from the 12th to the 900dth order of distances, should also be gradually of a different construction, with regard to physical size and brightness, from those which we see with the naked eye.

From the great diameter of the mirror of the 40 feet telescope we have reason to believe, that a review of the milky way with this instrument

[a] [These are all fields of varying degrees of richness in unobscured regions of the Milky Way, though not especially remarkable.—D.]

would carry the extent of this brilliant arrangement of stars as far into space as its penetrating power can reach, which would be to the 2300dth order of distances, and that it would then probably leave us again in the same uncertainty as the 20 feet telescope. . . .

## X. *Concluding Remarks.*

What has been said of the extent and condition of the milky way in several of my papers on the construction of the heavens, with the addition of the observations contained in this attempt to give a more correct idea of its profundity in space, will nearly contain all the general knowledge we can ever have of this magnificent collection of stars. To enter upon the subject of the contents of the heavens in the two comparatively vacant spaces on each side adjoining the milky way, the situation of globular clusters of planetary nebulæ, and of far extended nebulosities, would greatly exceed the compass of this Paper; I shall therefore only add one remarkable conclusion that may be drawn from the experiments which have been made with the gaging powers.

In fig. 11, let a circle, drawn with the radius of the 12th order of distances, represent a sphere containing every star that can be seen by

FIG. 11.

the naked eye; then, if the breadth of the milky way were only 5 degrees, and if its profundity did not exceed the 900dth order of distances, the two parallel lines in the figure, representing the breadth of the milky way, will, on each side of the centre of the inclosed circle, extend to more than the 39th order of distances.

From this it follows, that not only our sun, but all the stars we can see with the eye, are deeply immersed in the milky way, and form a component part of it.

WILLIAM HERSCHEL.

Slough, near Windsor,
May 10, 1817.

Herschel's farewell contribution to the study of the construction of the heavens[15]—and his last published paper except for a list of double stars for the newly founded Astronomical Society—was to extend to star clusters the technique of the equalization of starlight. With an ambiguous object—which might be either a near nebula or a distant cluster or galaxy—nothing could be done, but where stars could be discerned in a cluster then the distance of the cluster could be fixed by the distance of one of these stars. Likewise, if a cluster of known distance was visible as an ambiguous object in a telescope of low penetrating power, then the distance at which such an object could be detected (as ambiguous) in a *larger* instrument could be calculated from a comparison of the two powers involved.

The paper requires no new concepts, but it displays all Herschel's confidence and familiarity in handling his material, the theoretical calculation of vast distances no less than the frequent references to descriptions dictated at the telescope. He ends in characteristic style:

The 75th of the *Connoissance* [that is, of Messier's catalogue] is not visible to the eye, but may be seen in the finder; and the telescopic observations of it have ascertained its profundity to be of the 734th order; the station to which it should be brought, that it might be visible to the eye, is therefore of the 183·5th order. From this it follows, that with any telescope which has the space-penetrating power of the front view of my 20 feet reflector, this cluster might still be perceived if it were removed to the distance of the 13707th order; and that the 40 feet telescope, which in this case would really act the part of a finder, would still show this cluster of stars as an ambiguous object at a profundity in space amounting to the 35175th order.

# Chapter Six

# *Retrospect*

T OWARDS the end of his life Herschel's reputation among astronomers was second to none. It could hardly be otherwise, if only because of the great range of his interests, the enormous quantity of factual evidence he had accumulated, and the excitement aroused by such striking discoveries as those of Uranus and of binary systems. Yet in many ways he was isolated from his contemporaries. In purely physical terms this isolation would be easy to exaggerate, though his reluctance to miss opportunities for viewing during the sweeping period and, later, increasing infirmity restricted his travel, and his letter-writing tended to be sporadic and uncertain. But there were few if any who could compare with him in experience as an observer of the stars, and no one else had such powerful instruments. "Comme personne n'avoit, ou ne croyoit avoir d'instrument assez fort pour distinguer ces merveilles", wrote Cassini in 1784, "il fallut y croire sur sa parole."[1] Authors were reduced to reporting Herschel's words: "Dr. Herschel tells us . . . ":[2] "M. Herschel . . . nous assure qu'à l'aide des grossissemens étonnans que ses téléscopes supportent, il est parvenu a voir . . . ."[3]

This alone ruled out any real partnership with "unser neue Galilei"[4] when it came to interpreting observations, but there were more profound causes at work which restricted his contemporary influence and reveal him as a somewhat tragic figure. For, as he himself wrote, "a knowledge of the construction of the heavens has always been the ultimate object of my observations",[5] and yet, for all the profound importance of the questions he asked and the methods he developed, his achievement measured in terms of his contribution to established knowledge of its construction bore little relation to his Herculean efforts.

For this there are, as we have seen, a variety of reasons, many of them linked with the incorporation into his early theories of components which later proved to be weak if not actually faulty. His mapping of the Galaxy stood or fell with two postulates, each of which he was later forced to abandon. His confident early work on the distribution of nebulæ and star clusters drew its strength from his belief that all unresolved nebulæ were distant star clusters. When evidence forced him to reverse this opinion he was robbed of his linear dimension of distance: a *large* unresolved nebula was probably near rather than far, but this was all one could confidently say, and Herschel actually mistook many distant galaxies for small, near-by nebulæ. And all this time he had to contend with the methodological problem of inferring change from static evidence.

Of fundamental importance to him was his lifelong attempt to provide a third dimension to the stars, in which failure of the double-star method restricted him to inferring distance from brightness. We have seen how he solved the practical photometric problem only at the end of his life, and that meanwhile he took the traditional magnitudes as direct measures of distance, avoiding the possible test based on the Halley model, ignoring the opposing conclusions of other astronomers, and resisting such warnings as that of his friend Professor Vince of Cambridge, that "in respect to the magnitudes, the arrangement of that is merely arbitrary".[6] Still more revealing is his attitude to the 'brightness equals nearness' postulate. Crucial as it was to his work, he clung to it through thick and thin in defiance of the growing body of contrary evidence, from Michell's work on star systems, from his own binary stars, from the enormous proper motion of 61 Cygni. As for other astronomers, in 1782

Maskelyne had told him the principle seemed "a very hard hypothesis and not agreable to the great variety observable in the works of nature".[7] In 1797 Vince wrote, "But we have no reason whatever for making the . . . supposition, and if we reason from the bodies in our own system, analogy will be against it."[8] So with the years the chorus of dissent grew, until in 1833 John Herschel said of the counts made of stars of given magnitudes:

> The apparent "magnitude" of any star will, it is evident, depend 1st, on the star's distance from us; 2nd, on the absolute magnitude of its illuminated surface; 3rd, on the intrinsic brightness of that surface. Now, as we know nothing, or next to nothing, of any of these data, and have every reason for believing that each of them may differ in different individuals, in the proportion of *many millions to one* [our italics], it is clear that we are not to expect much satisfaction in any conclusions we may draw from numerical statements of the number of individuals arranged in our artificial classes.[9]

At the heart of the matter lay Herschel's quality of perseverance that could so easily degenerate into sheer obstinacy. In the great period of the 1780s, when he developed his statistical techniques for mapping the Galaxy and discerning the solar motion and when he created his first synthesis of the evolution of star systems, he made the assumptions necessary to his work boldly yet in reasonable conformity with the evidence then available to him. Some of these assumptions he was later forced to abandon, but in accordance with his admitted preference for theorizing too much rather than too little he did his best to replace them, though his theoretical constructions were irretrievably weakened in the process. Other assumptions, notably the fundamental 'brightness equals nearness' and traditional magnitudes postulates, he went to grotesque lengths to retain —for to part with them would be to bring his life's work to a halt. Coming to astronomy in middle age, he has been described as working as though he had few tomorrows: inflexibly resolved to carry his programmes to a successful conclusion, he could not afford to theorize with prudent restraint, nor could he reconcile himself to the centuries of observations others thought necessary for the understanding of the construction of the heavens. So it is not surprising that he failed to carry with him astronomers less driven by ambition: they sensibly preferred to wait and see.

Beyond the limits however of our own system, all at present is obscurity. Some vast and general views of the construction of the heavens, and the laws which may regulate the formation and motions of sidereal systems, have, it is true, been struck out; but, like the theories of the earth which have so long occupied the speculations of geologists, they remain to be supported or refuted by the slow accumulation of a mass of facts: and it is here . . . that the advantages of associated labour will appear more eminently conspicuous.

(From the Address of the Astronomical Society of London, explanatory of their views and objects, 1820.[10])

# Bibliography and Notes

Except for some early papers read before the Bath Philosophical Society, a small number read before the Royal Society but unpublished, and one (his last) which appeared in the first volume of *Memoirs of the Astronomical Society*, all Herschel's work appeared in the *Philosophical Transactions of the Royal Society* between 1780 and 1818. The text of this edition follows that of the *Philosophical Transactions*, except for the renumbering of figures and occasional changes of punctuation. Herschel's complete papers were reprinted in 1912 in two magnificent volumes entitled *The Scientific Papers of Sir William Herschel*, edited by J. L. E. Dreyer (London, 1912; this work is abbreviated below to 'Dreyer').

Passages from the original drafts of Herschel's published papers are copied from the manuscripts by permission of the Royal Society. Originals of many letters to Herschel, and copies of letters from him, are in the Library of the Royal Astronomical Society; some of these are reprinted in *The Herschel Chronicle* by Constance A. Lubbock (Cambridge, 1933; abbreviated to '*Chronicle*'). Except where indicated, all quotations from letters are taken from documents in the Library of the Royal Astronomical Society. This Library also contains much other Herschel material, described in an article by Dreyer in *Monthly Notices of the Royal Astronomical Society*, LXXVIII (1917–18), 547–54. The remaining books and papers were sold piecemeal at Sotheby's in 1958; important papers are now in the possession of the University of Texas, and of the Linda Hall Library, Kansas City.

Four biographies of Herschel have appeared in the last decade: J. B. Sidgwick's highly readable *William Herschel: Explorer of the Heavens* (London, 1953); Angus Armitage's analytical study, *William Herschel* (London, 1962); my own short *William Herschel: Pioneer of Sidereal Astronomy* (London, 1959); and, in German, *William Herschel, Leben und Werk* by G. Buttmann (Stuttgart, 1961). A valuable bibliography of the earlier works on Herschel is given in E. S. Holden's *Sir William Herschel: his life and works* (London, 1881). Of these earlier works, much the most important are: *W. Herschels Sämmtliche Schriften*: 1-ster Band. *Ueber den Bau des Himmels*, ed. J. W. Pfaff (Dresden and Leipzig, 1828); "Analyse historique et critique de la vie et des travaux de Sir William Herschel" by D. J. F. Arago, in *Annuaire du Bureau des Longitude* for 1842, 249–608; and F. G. W. Struve's *Études d'astronomie stellaire* (St. Petersburg, 1847).

There is a useful collation of Herschel's original catalogue numbers with N.G.C. numbers by H. D. Curtis, in *Handbuch der Astrophysik*, v–2 (1933), 910.

### Notes for Chapter One: The Natural History of the Heavens
### (pp. 13–26)

1. *Phil. Trans.*, LXXI (1781), 492–3; Dreyer, I, 30.
1a. *Correspondance littéraire* I (Paris, 1801), 97.
2. "Herschel's researches on the structure of the heavens", *Occasional Notes of the Royal Astronomical Society*, I (1938–41), 27–32, p. 30.
3. Letter of 25 December 1781.
4. *Chronicle*, 144.
5. *Phil. Trans.*, LXXIII (1783), 249–50; Dreyer, I, 108.
6. *Chronicle*, 138.
7. See note 1 for Chapter V.
8. *Phil. Trans.*, LXX (1780), 338–44; Dreyer, I, 1–4.
9. *Phil. Trans.*, LXXIII (1783), 474–82.
10. *Phil. Trans.*, LX (1760), 498–504.
11. *Phil. Trans.*, XXX (1717–18), 736–8.
12. *Chronicle*, 65–8, 87–9.
13. *Phil. Trans.*, XCVII (1807), 180–233; XCIX (1809), 259–302; C (1810), 149–77: Dreyer, II, 368–98, 414–40, 441–58.
14. *Chronicle*, 5.
15. *Ibid.*, 15.
16. *Ibid.*, 59.
17. Dreyer, I, xix.
18. *Chronicle*, 50.
19. Dreyer, I, xxii and xxiv.
20. Quoted in J. B. Sidgwick, *William Herschel*, 49.
20a. F. de Zach, "Sur la nouvelle planète Ouranus", *Nouveaux Mémoires de l'Académie . . . de Bruxelles: Sciences et Arts*, I (1788), 22–48, p. 25.

In 1830 a disk of pure flint glass under one foot in diameter cost £1000 (James Sime, *William Herschel and his work* (Edinburgh, 1900), 109).

21. Dreyer, I, xxiv.
22. *A Compleat System of Opticks*, II, 447.
23. *Ibid.*, 454.
24. *Ibid.*, 447–8.
25. *Astronomy explained upon Sir Isaac Newton's principles*, 2nd edition (1757), pp. 77, 231.
26. *Ibid.*, 230.
27. *Ibid.*, 237.
28. *Ibid.*, 236–7.
29. *Ibid.*, 1st edition (1756), pp. 5, 30.
30. Notably in his paper "On the Nature and Construction of the Sun and fixed Stars", *Phil. Trans.*, LXXXV (1795), 46–72; Dreyer, I, 470–84.
31. *Astronomy*, 2nd edition, p. 5.
32. *Ibid.*, 61–2.
33. See, for example, *Chronicle*, 79.
34. *Chronicle*, 75.
35. See the letters written by Watson to Herschel in the critical period between the discovery of Uranus and the award of the royal pension to Herschel.
36. Dreyer, I, xc; *Chronicle*, 76–7.
37. Letter of 25 December 1781.
38. *Chronicle*, 82–3.
39. Letter from Watson, 18 December 1781. Aubert offered to accompany Herschel there (letters of 22 January 1782 and 18 January 1785).
40. Letter of 7 September 1789.
41. Including Maskelyne (letters of Watson, 25 December 1781 and 11 January 1782).
42. For example, letter of 25 December 1781.
43. As sent with letter of 7 December 1781.
44. Letter of 4 January 1782.
45. As shown by Herschel's original version of his paper "On the Parallax of the fixed Stars", Library of the Royal Society.
46. *Chronicle*, 115.
47. Especially letters of June 1782.
48. See *Phil. Trans.*, CIV (1814), 275, and CV (1815), 295–6; Dreyer, II, 536 and 543.

*Notes for Chapter Two: Double Stars and the Motion of the Sun*
(pp. 27–59)

1. "A proposal for discovering the annual parallax of Sirius", *Phil. Trans.*, LI (1760), 889–95, p. 889.

2. *Dialogue of the Great World Systems*, third day (ed. G. de Santillana (Chicago, 1953), 392).

3. "A letter to the Right honourable George Earl of Macclesfield concerning an apparent Motion observed in some of the fixed Stars", read 14 February 1747; *Phil. Trans.*, XLV (1748), 1–43, p. 41.

4. Letter of 7 December 1781.

5. *Chronicle*, 87.

6. *Phil. Trans.*, LXXII (1782), 82–111; Dreyer, I, 39–57.

7. Only partly reproduced in *Chronicle*, 109–10.

8. *Phil. Trans.*, LXXII (1782), 104–5; Dreyer, I, 52.

9. Herschel's reply to this criticism is reproduced in *Chronicle*, 110.

10. *Chronicle*, 87.

11. *Phil. Trans.*, LVII (1767), 234–64.

12. *Ibid.*, 240–1.

13. *Traité d'optique sur la gradation de la lumiere* (2nd edition, Paris, 1760). English translation by W. E. Knowles Middleton, *Pierre Bouguer's Optical Treatise on the Gradation of Light* (Toronto, 1961).

14. *Phil. Trans.*, LVII (1767), 241.

15. *Ibid.*, 242.

16. *Phil. Trans.*, LXXII (1782), 105; Dreyer, I, 52.

17. *Phil. Trans.*, XCII (1802), 484; Dreyer, II, 203.

18. *Phil. Trans.*, XXXI (1720–1), 24–6.

19. *Phil. Trans.*, LVII (1767), 246–50.

20. Letter dated 26 May 1783, published in *Phil. Trans.*, LXXIV (1784), 35–57, p. 56.

21. *Phil. Trans.*, LXXII (1782), 161; Dreyer, I, 90.

21a. See also letter of Bode to Herschel, 13 August 1785; *Astronomisches Jahrbuch* for 1787 (1784), 252, and for 1789 (1786), 245; and J. J. le F. Lalande, *Astronomie*, 1 (3rd ed., Paris, 1792), 270.

22. "Account of the Changes that have happened during the last Twenty-five Years, in the relative Situation of Double-stars", *Phil. Trans.*, XCIII (1803), 339–82; Dreyer, II, 250–76. "Continuation of an Account of the Changes that have happened in the relative Situation of double Stars", *Phil. Trans.*, XCIV (1804), 353–84; Dreyer, II, 277–96.

23. *Phil. Trans.*, XCII (1802), 480–6; Dreyer, II, 201–4.

24. See his discussions of ε Bootis, ζ Aquarii, ε Lyræ, South-preceding Fl. 30 Orionis, and Rigel, in the papers cited.

25. *Phil. Trans.*, LVII (1767), 237.
26. *Phil. Trans.*, XCVI (1806), 215; Dreyer, II, 344.
27. *Phil. Trans.*, LXXV (1785), 48; Dreyer, I, 172.
28. *Phil. Trans.*, XCIII (1803), 366; Dreyer, II, 265.
29. *Phil. Trans.*, LXXII (1782), 115; Dreyer, I, 60.
30. *Phil. Trans.*, LXXII (1782), 122; Dreyer, I, 64.
31. *Phil. Trans.*, XCIV (1804), 361; Dreyer, II, 282.
32. S. Vince, *A complete system of astronomy*, I (Cambridge, 1797), 493.
33. *Monatliche Correspondenz*, XXVI (1812), 148–63, 61 Cygni was to be cited many times as evidence against Herschel's principle.
34. *Phil. Trans.*, LXXII (1782), 103; Dreyer, I, 51. In his 1803 and 1804 papers on changes in double stars, Herschel uses the solar motion to explain some of his observations.
35. Letter of Maskelyne to Herschel, 19 April 1782, and Herschel's reply, 28 April 1782.
36. See Herschel's letter of 3 March 1783 to Alexander Wilson, and letter of Schroeter to Herschel, January 1784.
37. *Phil. Trans.*, XLV (1748), 40.
38. Cited by Herschel at the end of the postscript to his paper, *Phil. Trans.*, LXXIII (1783), 282; Dreyer, I, 130.
39. *Phil. Trans.*, LVII (1767), 252–3.
40. Letter of 15 March 1783.
41. Letter of 17 March 1783.
42. His new direction for solar motion is first announced in his discussion of α Herculis in the second paper (1804) on changes observed in double stars (note 22).
43. "On the Direction and Velocity of the Motion of the Sun, and Solar System", *Phil. Trans.*, XCV (1805), 233–56; Dreyer, II, 317–31.
44. "On the Quantity and Velocity of the Solar Motion", *Phil. Trans.*, XCVI (1806), 205–37; Dreyer, II, 338–59.
45. *Phil. Trans.*, XCVI (1806), 217; Dreyer, II, 346–7.
46. *Phil. Trans.*, XCV (1805), 234–5; Dreyer, II, 318.
47. *Phil. Trans.*, XCVI (1806), 224; Dreyer, II, 351–2.
48. See under "Lustre of the Stars in Orion", in "A Third Catalogue of the comparative Brightness of the Stars", *Phil. Trans.*, LXXXVII (1797), 293–324, pp. 320–2; Dreyer, I, 582.
49. *Phil. Trans.*, XCV (1805), 239; Dreyer, II, 320.
50. *Phil. Trans.*, XCV (1805), 243; Dreyer, II, 323.
51. *Phil. Trans.*, LXXIII (1783), 275; Dreyer, I, 126.
52. *Elements of astronomy* (2nd. ed., London, 1819), 130.

53. "On the proper motion of the fixed stars", published in *Memoirs of the Royal Astronomical Society*, V (1833), 147-70, p. 155.

54. E. S. Holden, *Sir William Herschel*, 154.

*Notes for Chapter Three: The Construction of the Heavens: the first synthesis (pp. 60-116)*

1. "An account of several Nebulæ or lucid Spots like Clouds", *Phil. Trans.*, XXIX (1715-16), 390-2, p. 390.

2. *Phil. Trans.*, LVII (1767), 251.

3. *Ibid.*, 261.

4. Letter of 7 December 1781.

5. Letter of 18 May 1784.

6. "Observations of Messier's nebulæ and clusters", Library of the R.A.S.

7. Letter to Wilson, 8 March 1784.

8. Letter of 17 March 1785.

9. In 1802 he wrote, "I am now convinced, by a long inspection and continued examination of it, that the milky-way itself consists of stars very differently scattered from those which are immediately about us. . . . The stars of which it is composed are very unequally scattered, and shew evident marks of clustering together in many separate allotments" (*Phil. Trans.*, XCII (1802), 480, 495; Dreyer, II, 200, 211).

10. Astonishing Struve by so doing (*Études d'astronomie stellaire*, note 52).

11. 1952 edition (New York), 402.

12. See *The Leibniz-Clarke Correspondence*, ed. by H. G. Alexander (Manchester, 1956).

13. *Histoire et théorie de la terre* (Paris, 1749)=vol. I of *Histoire naturelle*.

14. *Époques de la nature* (Paris, 1778).

15. *Phil. Trans.*, CVIII (1818), 453; Dreyer, II, 602.

16. *Phil. Trans.*, LXXVIII (1788), 368; Dreyer, I, 319.

17. J. Lexell, "Disquisitio de investiganda parallaxi Solis, ex transitu Veneris per Solem anno 1769", *Novi Commentarii*, XVII (1772), 609-72; cited in H. Woolf, *The Transits of Venus* (Princeton, 1959), 191.

18. *Phil. Trans.*, LXXXV (1795), 63; Dreyer, I, 480.

19. Dreyer, I, cv.

20. *Phil. Trans.*, LXXXV (1795), 49; Dreyer, I, 472.

21. f. 67 (Linda Hall Library notebook).

22. Woolf, *op. cit.*, 208.

23. *Phil. Trans.*, LXXIII (1783), 14; Dreyer, I, 107.

24. *Phil. Trans.*, XCV (1805), 235; Dreyer, II, 318.

*Notes for Chapter Four: The Construction of the Heavens: true
nebulosity and the second synthesis* (pp. 117–162)

1. See footnote to p. 68.
2. *Phil. Trans.*, XCII (1802), 499; Dreyer, II, 213.
3. Letter of Schroeter to Herschel, December 1797.
4. "Catalogue of 500 new Nebulæ, nebulous Stars, planetary Nebulæ, and Clusters of Stars; with Remarks on the Construction of the Heavens", *Phil. Trans.*, XCII (1802), 477–528; Dreyer, II, 199–234.
5. *Phil. Trans.*, XCII (1802), 477–8; Dreyer, II, 199.
6. *Phil. Trans.*, XCII (1802), 499; Dreyer, II, 213.
7. *Phil. Trans.*, XCII (1802), 498–9; Dreyer, II, 213.
8. Letter of 17 July 1814.
9. *Chronicle*, 197.
10. 269–71.
11. *Études d'astronomie stellaire*, 48.
12. *Memoirs of the Astronomical Society of London*, II (1826), 487–8.

*Notes for Chapter Five: The Final Fathoming*
(pp. 163–187)

1. *Phil. Trans.*, LXXXVI (1796), 166–226 and 452–82, LXXXVII (1797), 293–324, LXXXIX (1799), 121–44, Series A, CCV (1906), 399–477; Dreyer, I, 530–84, II, 22–30 and 628–49.
2. See note 13 to Chapter Two above.
3. Dreyer, I, lxviii.
4. *Phil. Trans.*, LXXV (1785), 127–36.
5. *Phil. Trans.*, XCVI (1806), 208; Dreyer, II, 339.
6. *Phil. Trans.*, XXXI (1720–1), 25.
7. See note 9 to Chapter Three above.
8. *Phil. Trans.*, LXXXVI (1796), 166–8; Dreyer, I, 530–1.
9. *Phil. Trans.*, XC (1800), 49–85; Dreyer, II, 31–52.
10. *Phil. Trans.*, XC (1800), 63; Dreyer, II, 39.
11. *Phil. Trans.*, XCVI (1806), 214; Dreyer, II, 343.
12. "Mars und Aldebaran", in *Monatliche Correspondenz*, VIII (1803), 293–311.
13. *Phil. Trans.*, XC (1800), 83–5; Dreyer, II, 50–2.
14. *Phil. Trans.*, CVIII (1818), 463; Dreyer, II, 609.
15. "Astronomical observations and experiments, selected for the purpose of ascertaining the relative distances of clusters of stars, and of investigating how far the power of our telescopes may be expected to reach into space, when directed to ambiguous celestial objects", *Phil. Trans.*, CVIII (1818), 429–70; Dreyer, II, 592–613.

*Notes for Chapter Six: Retrospect*
(pp. 188–191)

1. *Mémoires de l'Académie Royale des Sciences* (1784), 333.
2. John Brinkley, *Elements of astronomy* (2nd ed., London, 1819), 24.
3. F. T. Schubert, *Traité d'astronomie théorique* (French trans., St. Petersburg, 1822), II, 37.
4. *Monatliche Correspondenz*, V (1802), 74.
5. Above, p. 133.
6. S. Vince, *A complete system of astronomy*, I (Cambridge, 1797), 493.
7. Letter of 19 April 1782.
8. *A complete system of astronomy*, I, 493.
9. *A treatise on astronomy* (London, 1833), 374.
10. *Memoirs of the Astronomical Society of London*, I (1822–5), 4.